D0275514

Fairy Tales for Millennials

BRUNO VINCENT

Fairy Tales
for
Millennials

PENGUIN BOOKS

PENGUIN BOOKS

UK | USA | Canada | Ireland | Australia
India | New Zealand | South Africa

Penguin Books is part of the Penguin Random House group of companies
whose addresses can be found at global.penguinrandomhouse.com.

www.penguin.co.uk
www.puffin.co.uk
www.ladybird.co.uk

First published 2019

001

Set in 11.5/15pt Minion Pro
Typeset by Jouve (UK), Milton Keynes
Printed and bound in Great Britain by Clays Ltd, Elcograf S.p.A.

A CIP catalogue record for this book is available from the British Library

ISBN: 978–0–241–42423–0

All correspondence to:
Penguin Books
Penguin Random House Children's
80 Strand, London WC2R 0RL

To Henry, Juliette and family with all my love

Contents

SNOW WHITE

'Yes, ma'am, you're an absolute QILF.'

In a distant land there once dwelled a queen. Her beloved husband had died many years before, and she had been left to rule the kingdom alone. Each morning, she stood before her ornate gilt mirror and spoke the same words:

'Mirror, mirror, on the wall, who is the fairest of them all?'

'All right,' said the mirror. 'Top stories! Remember Mother Hubbard? How she looks now will AMAZE you . . .'

'No, no,' said the queen. 'I'm not interested in that stuff.'

'Humpté Dumpté in intensive care after trying to scale border wall . . .'

'Please, mirror . . .'

'Rumpelstiltskin's lawyer issues a statement denying any wrongdoing as another twenty-six maidens come forward . . .'

'Mirror, I *beseech* you. No more.'

'Sorry, Your Grace,' the mirror said. 'Forgot who I was talking to. Everyone else loves that stuff.'

'Be that as it may,' the queen said, 'just tell me who is the fairest.'

'Bear with me. Accessing Kingdom Equality Index . . .'

While she waited, the queen touched up her hair in the mirror and thought about the sweeping changes she had implemented in the kingdom. Her departed hubby, missed as he was, *had* been a bit of a dinosaur. So, no sooner had the last tray of funereal canapés been deposited in the castle's voluminous recycling caddy than the queen had begun drawing up plans to make Fairyland a better place to live.

First to go were the outdated expectations that everyone had to do the same job as their parents. The daughter of a dairymaid, for instance, need not feel that her future stretched monotonously ahead of her, milking Penelope and Bluebell and warding off the advances of rough-handed farm boys.

Thanks to systems put in place by the queen, she could now access further education and get qualifications to improve her lot. Through hard work, she might pass her exams and become – a physiotherapist, perhaps, or a lecturer in fine art. (Although she oughtn't expect the unwanted advances to suddenly cease.)

Gone also was the patriarchal system of preferment. Slightly more than half the positions in court were now filled by women, and the ethnicity of those who held office reflected (as accurately as could possibly be determined) the demographics of the populace.

Despite a few early mutterings, people quickly realized the benefits of a decision-making apparatus that more closely reflected the society it served, and all protestations melted away. A wider range of perspectives were heard and understood, policy implementation and communication were enormously improved, and the government as a whole ran with a humming efficiency unknown in previous ages.

The formerly rigid hierarchy learned to flex and bend, and in one bold leap the concept of social mobility moved from the merely possible to a gleaming actuality.

Put simply: things functioned, and people were happy.

But the queen didn't stop there. Old texts and stories that promoted outmoded values were brought up to date. Mary's lamb was allowed to go everywhere with her and was officially registered as an emotional-support animal. The tortoise and the hare were deemed both to deserve a medal simply for competing in the race. And the boy who cried wolf was diagnosed with truth-aversion disorder and sent on a course of counselling.

Everyone agreed that these new versions were a huge improvement – partly, of course, because there wasn't much option but to do so. There may have been the occasional grimace or raised eyebrow from the old folks, but that was the behaviour of old folks throughout the ages. (After all, had *their* grandparents not looked askance, too, at the great advances of *their* day: granting women the same rights as horses, fizzy beer and actual doctors?) But the grumbling was minimal, and the large majority celebrated that their society was more equal and just.

The queen (Queen Generous was her name – Gennie for short) enjoyed great popularity. When she wasn't opening a new ward at the local hospital or auctioning off her old gowns for charity, she would cast her gaze around the kingdom (*realm*, rather) in search of further ways to improve life for her subjects. Or, at least, for those subjects who were not unfairly benefitting from the unhappiness and poverty of others.

And so, as she stood waiting in front of her magical mirror on this sunny morning, she was not without a little complacency. The mirror – an antique – was still growing accustomed to its new settings, and sometimes got mixed up when accessing the Fairness Index. (The fact that the mirror still occasionally defaulted to equating 'fairness' with being blonde, underfed and twenty-two may have had something to do with her husband's private browsing settings, but the queen chose not to think about this.) However she didn't mind waiting, because no matter how long it took, there was only one face the mirror ever showed under the banner 'Most Fair': the queen's own.

So she was bemused rather than angry to find herself looking at another's face. 'Mirror,' she said patiently. 'Is there something wrong? I feel sure the palace coffers can stretch to a *new* mirror . . .'

But the mirror, usually so happy to jest and cajole, remained formal. 'There is no error, Your Grace,' it said. 'What you see is the truth. Snow White is the fairest in all the land.'

Now, I have not mentioned Snow White up to this point. You might happen to think that's down to laziness or bad storytelling. You might on the other hand mutter to yourself, 'Snow White, eh? And not the queen, as expected!' and mark it down as a rather snazzy rug-pull on my part. I shan't try to persuade you either way; we all have to live our own truth.

Nevertheless, here she is now. Snow White! The daughter of the dead king by a former marriage, and doted upon adoringly by her father up to his dying breath. Gossips in court liked to speculate that this ate at the new queen, and that she was jealous of her stepdaughter – who, the gossips added, was a *hard* ten, seriously hot even by palace standards. There *must* be (these gossips concluded, clearly having too much time on their hands) a very serious rivalry between the two.

And now the mirror was saying that Snow White was the fairest? It was a bitter blow.

The queen was *certain* the mirror must be mistaken. She switched the mirror off and on again, and ran the calculations a second and a third time.

As the mirror's voice reeled off the remarkable list of Snow White's achievements, the queen went pale. The queen knew Snow White (her name another unfortunate legacy of the unreconstructed king) had spent years travelling the land, helping the poor and unfortunate. But she hadn't realized exactly how much the princess had accomplished.

It seemed Snow White had used her meagre royal allowance to set up a family planning centre in the city slums. She'd secured sponsorship from a major quill manufacturer for a grant scheme for emerging writers from underprivileged backgrounds and distant provinces. She'd also established a Universal Court of Historical Justice to examine claims of historical land theft and ethnic cleansing by the first human settlers against the indigenous swamp goblins.

Furthermore, she had declared her intention to dismantle the monarchy entirely, replacing it with a representational democracy and universal suffrage, perhaps with a vestigial *constitutional* monarchy, to encourage tourism – if such should be the wish of the people.

Once these projects were complete, the business of wealth redistribution could commence.

Everyone was going crazy for Snow White's initiatives. Of course they were.

As she reached the end of the list, Queen Gennie was no longer pale. Her face flushed. Her blood boiled.

'Alexa!' she bellowed. 'Find Snow White at once. And tell her to come here.'

Queen Gennie waited until she was quite sure Alexa had gone and there was complete silence in her chambers. Then she muttered quietly to the mirror to show her the story about Mother Hubbard. In what way could her appearance these days *possibly* be amazing? She'd looked ancient twenty years ago . . .

When the servant finally found Snow White, she was at the Poor School (although you weren't supposed to call it that any more – it was the Bright Smiles Academy), reading *Let Their Squeaks Rise Up*, the popular old book whose official title was now *The Three Mice Whose Ability to See or Otherwise Is Not the Only Important Thing About Them, Quite Frankly*.

Snow White had just reached the scene where the farmer's wife breaks down in the witness box and confesses everything. It was she, after all, who had assaulted the victims. They had not faked their injuries to receive benefits, as the evil newspapers owned by Lord Murdlock had claimed. Cheers were about to fill the courtroom: the victims' application for damages was legitimate!

'Queen wants to see you,' Alexa interrupted, right at the best part of the scene. The children groaned in disappointment.

A little put out to be cut off in mid flow like this, Snow White glanced at Alexa, who as always remained expressionless. 'She sounded cross,' Alexa added.

'Don't you worry. I'll be back in a moment,' Snow White said to her students. 'Now, Alexa, I know my way to the palace. Perhaps you could take over the reading . . .'

As the servant (or domestic-assistance executive, to give her proper job title) took up the book, the children groaned again. Alexa's voice was so monotone. Meanwhile, Snow White was hurrying out of the door.

When Snow White reached the queen's chambers, she found Her Grace standing at a window looking thoughtful. Beside her was an incongruous fellow. He was rough-looking. Mud and straw clung to the hem of his tunic, and at Snow White's arrival he turned towards her with a barbaric leer.

Snow White quailed as she saw the blunt-edged hatchet in his hand – and, on the queen's face, cold determination.

Months passed, and spring turned to summer. Nothing was heard of Snow White, and in the Equality Index, the mirror reported the queen was back in her spot at the top of the pops.

Tongues wagged around the palace, as always. A petition calling to investigate the princess's disappearance gained a few hundred signatures, then fizzled out. There were dark murmurings over pints of ale in the Hare and Hounds (whose sign had been repainted to show the animals clinking tankards together, best of friends). But the good works continued, the populace got happier day by day, and the whispers eventually subsided.

Everywhere, that is, except for a cosy cottage in a corner of the forest where Tuesdays were burrito night.

Shortly after 6 p.m., the cottage's seven inhabitants trooped in from work, tired and sweaty after another day in the mines. In previous ages they would have been covered in coal dust too – but that sort of work was done by machines these days. And besides being cleaner, data mining paid a whole lot more. After they had all showered and dressed, they ate their burritos – with many a tummy rumble and eructation – then popped a bottle of craft beer and shuffled next door to the sound-proofed studio.

'Testing, one two, one two,' said Lefty. 'Testing levels.'

'All good,' said Lispy, holding one of a pair of cans to his right ear. 'Ready to go.'

The others took this as a signal. They sat down round the table, put on their headphones, adjusted their mics, cleared their throats, licked their lips and waited patiently.

'And . . . rolling,' said Lispy.

'This podcast is brought to you by Dragondrop,' said Lefty. 'Whether you're writing a blog or building an online store, Dragondrop offers . . .'

The others had heard this bit a thousand times before. Well, sixty-odd times at least.

First, there had been their abortive debut podcast, in which they'd done episode recaps of *Game of Thrones*, but they soon realized everyone was in on that act. It was the oldest trick in the podcasting book.

When they turned their attention to an unsolved local mystery, their podcasting really took off. Now they had a dedicated following, sponsorship deals for razors, mattresses and audiobooks, and had even been booked to record live episodes at a sprinkling of summer festivals.

As the theme music – a repeated whistling refrain – faded, the podcast began. Lefty, the unspoken leader of the group, kicked things off.

'Hi ho, listeners!' he said. 'On this episode of *Blood Red*, the true crime podcast about the unsolved disappearance of Snow White, we'll be looking at new evidence, re-examining the known facts, and interviewing a very special guest.'

'That's right, Lefty,' said Lispy, with a slight lisp, before going on to detail the evidence on offer.

The others waited patiently. As hosts of the podcast, the seven housemates were known as Lefty, Lispy, Burpy, Clever Clogs, Stinky, Hesitant and The Monster. On the lease of the cottage, however, their names were Michael, Thomas, Dan, David, David, Anuvab and Gerald. After much discussion, the group had decided upon their 'stage names' as a branding exercise to make themselves more marketable. It had worked, after a fashion – but the only person who ever got asked for selfies was The Monster, a fact the other six resented ('and he's a quarter of an inch *shorter* than *me*,' Burpy often complained).

The 'new evidence' they were examining today was hardly earth-shattering. A relative of their key suspect – the Huntsman – claimed to have overheard expressions of republican sentiment in the Huntsman's family home when he was growing up. This didn't exactly transform the case because there was republican sentiment all over the shop these days (including in the palace – including from the *victim*).

Also, they had established to everyone's satisfaction by this point that the Huntsman was nobody's idea of a conspirator. It was doubtful he had the independence of thought to slice a loaf of bread of his own accord, let alone the guile and determination to lop off a princess's head. And that's not to say anything against his upbringing – his twin sisters were a law professor and a meteorologist, after all. If there *were* some sort of plot, Old Huntypoos was the dictionary definition of an unwitting patsy.

So much for the new evidence, then.

After making early progress in the case, the podcast had become popular, and even trended for a while. But that all seemed so long ago. They now sensed the crime was not going to be solved, and the podcast was outstaying its welcome.

Soon there would be another ghastly murder, and the next 'coolest new true crime podcast' would come along. It was an eventuality too horrible to contemplate. (They'd already heard whispers of a hot new show about two siblings called Jack and Jill, and the horrific events that allegedly unfolded on a remote hilltop.)

The next section of the podcast was spent revisiting revelations made in earlier episodes, and looking at the totality of evidence, to see if it offered a new perspective. There was the testimony of a travelling axe-sharpener; the financial irregularities in the forest management service; and the sightings of a pair of brothers in the area at the time, said to be named Grimm, who evinced a 'creepy fixation' with princesses.

This was all done in the most self-serving way possible, with constant references to how the podcast had galvanized a formerly moribund investigation.

Then, at long last, they came to today's guest.

'After all the leads we've chased that have proven to be dead ends,' said Stinky, 'I received a tip-off last night that led me to today's guest. Who, I assure you, is going to change *everything*.'

With that, the studio door swung open. A figure swept in.

The six others gasped. First at this bravura piece of showmanship (*Stinky's such a bloody pro*, thought Burpy. *He'll be wanting his own spin-off before long*), then at the elegance and beauty of their guest. She wore a floor-length velvet cape, whose hood she slid back to reveal tumbling raven-black curls, flawless skin and a rosebud mouth. She smiled demurely, and seven hearts broke as one.

'Sit here, next to me,' muttered The Monster, stamping on Lispy's toes and pulling up a chair before Hesitant could get his act together. 'Away from the smell of Stinky. Har har.'

'You *are* kind,' said the stranger, and they all noted she had excellent mic technique.

'Now, please,' said Stinky, 'tell us your tale.'

'Well, you see, it's all been such a big misunderstanding,' said Snow White, for it was she. She told them how she had been sent deep into the woods with the Huntsman those many months before to oversee the planning and construction of an entire new village, complete with the latest accessibility equipment and a sports park for Paralympics events. It was only to be unveiled once it was finished.

It hadn't been a murder at all.

In fact, it was all part of a plot (at first Queen Gennie's, but later with Snow White's input too) to bring harmony to the entire forest – because this project was for animals as well as humans. It included shelters, hospitals, libraries, municipal baths and food banks, community fridges and free canteens for all. Not to mention the gymnasiums, swimming pools, sports parks, playgrounds and landscaped pleasure gardens.

'And so that's why I'm here with you all today,' Snow White said. 'To announce that, as of this moment, Village-in-the-Woods is officially open.'

The episode was, of course, a killer.

Never before had a true crime show had the victim walk in, hale and hearty, and introduce themselves in the final reel. *Blood Red* shot straight to the top of the charts and stayed there for months. There was talk of an extended live tour (following in the footsteps of the smash hit *My Dad Illustrated a Lewd Manuscript*), a podcast-themed IPA and even branded jerkins.

Of course, any envy that Queen Gennie might have felt towards Snow White when she had seen her stepdaughter's face in the mirror had lasted mere seconds. The queen, a kind and thoughtful person, had immediately realized that the two women were stronger together. United, they made for a world-beating team.

What had made her go pale and then blush, was first the horror and then the shame that she had never realized before what a talented and determined woman her stepdaughter was. Truly it was a blessing. Now it was essential they make up for lost time . . .

As for the notion that she would ever compete with a younger woman out of something as basic as sexual jealousy? Ludicrous.

Thus they all lived. Not happily ever after, which everyone knows is unrealistic, but with much more sensible ambitions and manageable expectations of contentment that they could plan for and work towards together, as a populace.

Which is probably as good as you can have it. Right?

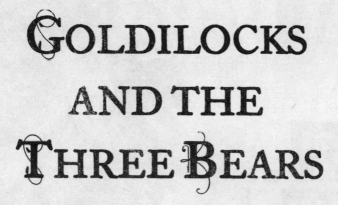

GOLDILOCKS
AND THE
THREE BEARS

*'Dad, is this what they mean by locally
sourced and free-range?'*

Once upon a time, a young woman called Goldilocks was out walking in the woods. She was all by herself because she was determined to make the best of her weekend, and all of her friends were away LARPing. (Goldie loved that her buddies were so enthusiastic, and right-on, and wouldn't object to going along to a Harry Potter-themed weekend, or, at a push, *The Lord of the Rings* – but role-playing *The Handmaid's Tale* was really where she had to draw the line.)

Away from the city she was enjoying the fresh air and wondering what all the beautiful flowers and trees were called, and thinking someone (she, perhaps!) ought to invent an app to help identify plants. Her mind was running on with the topics of seed funding, investment splits, office square footage and logo design when she found herself in front of an open door.

There was something charming about it, in that it was hidden in the bole of a tree, and that it opened right on to a gorgeous, *perfectly* fitted-out little woodland kitchen. Goldie wondered if it might be a themed Airbnb, or the set of an extremely cute Shakespeare-in-the-woods theatre-in-the-round. Or it could be a pop-up where they served food in weird new ways. Beans on a shovel, tea out of a hat, that sort of thing. Like that swamp goblin street food place everyone was raving about, recently opened in the giant shoe after the old lady and her children got rehoused by the village elders.

Whatever it was, she figured there was a chance that she would find a power point inside. Her phone was hovering around the fifteen per cent danger zone and she needed to charge it, or it might not see her home – a scenario that would make any law-abiding citizen consider breaking and entering. So in she went.

Nosing inside, Goldilocks failed to spot all the little details dotted around that betokened an *obviously* inhabited dwelling. A copy of *Bear Necessities* magazine left folded on a stool, the crossword half completed. Mugs proclaiming URSA MINOR, URSA MAJOR and GOLF IS MY SUPERPOWER hanging from hooks in the wall, beneath the names KEVIN, MUMMY and DADDY.

She noticed none of this. Instead she focused directly on the three steaming bowls of porridge she saw on the counter. You see, despite being barely twenty, Goldilocks had a tidy little career for herself posting on Impstagram about fun and exciting places to buy comfort food. If there was a novelty burger, an exotic toastie or some ingeniously served hot chocolate, she made it her business to know about it – then photograph it, consume it and post her thoughts within a beautifying cluster of emojis.

And this was no vanity project. Her followship (if that isn't a word, it ought to be – en masse she referred to her fans as Gold Diggers), had recently raced past the million mark and she was so well regarded as an influencer that there wasn't a single high-concept restaurant in Fairyland she didn't know about. Or so she had thought.

Goldilocks had been starting to feel that there was nothing left for her to write about – until she saw these three bowls of porridge. She had, it's true, recently covered a joint that served exclusively breakfast cereals, and one that did just plain toast. But she'd not yet exhausted the subject of porridge.

What's more, she now realized she was bloody hungry. This was meant to be.

Her antennae were up, and she inched forward, excited. She spent the next few minutes taking hundreds of shots from different heights and angles. There was a real art to this. The pics had to look convincingly casual, an effect that Goldilocks was prepared to go to enormous lengths to replicate.

So to the first bowl of porridge – or was it spelled porage? She made a mental note to check before posting. Best not risk annoying the entire population of Caledonia (or wherever) by accidentally slighting their national dish . . . Although, actually, a *tiny* bit of controversy could even help. Then she could post a tearfully heartfelt apology about how much she'd learned and changed, own the narrative, and look good into the bargain.

Lost in these reflections, she lifted the spoon and imbibed a mouthful of porridge. Her eyes bulged.

It was *piping hot.*

She panicked as the soft tissue of her mouth tried to cope with a glob of molten lead. Her only respite lay in the prospect of suing the maker of this diabolical substance – she noted with satisfaction there was no CAUTION: HOT sign visible.

Gradually, though, the pain subsided, and she was able to swallow the porridge. It wasn't actually half bad, in terms of flavour. She gasped and wiped a tear.

Goldilocks turned to the next bowl. She held up a spoonful gingerly and made a kissing mouth in case it was as hot as the first. Then felt self-conscious and looked round to see if she was being watched, but there was still no one in sight.

This time, there was no heat at all. The porridge was even unpleasantly cold. There was flavour in there, but without heat, the stodginess of the texture rose to the fore. *Gross.*

Finally, she tried the third bowl of porridge. This one was *perfect*. The model of what breakfast could be! There was a dash of cream mixed in, a sprinkle of salt, and a blob of delicious jam that was surely home-made. It was great. It was *compelling*. Pausing only to take twenty more pics, she wolfed the lot.

Her blood sugar returned to a satisfactory state, Goldilocks wandered in a happy daze into the bedroom next door, where she found a power point for her phone. She was quite sure no one could object to her using it. Having a charged phone was practically a human right.

As she waited for her phone to charge enough to see her home, she began to feel a little drowsy. There were three beds in the room, and she sat down on the nearest one. It was shockingly hard, with practically no give at all – like a wooden board! *Specially designed for someone with a back condition*, she thought.

She tried the next one and sank deep into the mattress with a scream. Then she giggled at her own silliness. It was soft as a pillow! Who could *possibly* get to sleep on such a thing?

She went and flopped on to the third bed, which was perfect for her – comfy but not too soft, and with only the slight fragrance of a decent conditioner instead of being slathered with the stuff like the soft bed had been.

Resting her head on the pillow, she studied the patterns on the ceiling. She'd just lie here for a minute. Maybe two . . .

'What the *hell*?'

Goldilocks woke up with a start.

Three bears were peering down at her.

'I'm s-so sorry,' she stammered, climbing off the bed. She blinked furiously, trying to orientate herself, then started to tuck in the sheets in a flustered and useless fashion.

'What the *hell*?' the biggest bear repeated. He was standing with his paws on his hips.

Next to him, his son was filming the whole thing on his phone, which only added to Goldie's confusion. It seemed it was the cub's bed that she'd been sleeping in.

'I must have fallen asleep . . .' she muttered.

'I can *see* that!' yelled Daddy Bear.

'He can see *that*, dear,' said Mummy Bear.

'Falling asleep is not the *issue*,' said Daddy Bear.

The other two bears shook their heads.

'The *issue* here,' Daddy Bear went on, somewhat remorselessly in Goldie's view, 'is this: what are you *doing* in our *house*?'

Goldilocks began to stammer again, but all her excuses were unutterably feeble. Instead, she began to cry.

'Well, now,' said Daddy Bear impatiently, while Mummy Bear came over to comfort her and wipe away her tears.

Back in the kitchen, the bears made Goldilocks a cup of cocoa, returned her phone, and heard her out, albeit sceptically – particularly Daddy Bear.

When it came to the fact that she was 'lost in the woods', she received an especially loud 'harrumph!' from Daddy Bear. It turned out the bears lived very close to the main road – scarcely a hundred yards away. It was a sore point for them, as the road was a noisy, dirty, dangerous nuisance. But it was the best they could afford in this part of the forest.

'That is some human privilege crap right there,' said Daddy Bear when Goldilocks finished her story. 'If a little bear your size was found nosing around in some human's bedroom, her furry ass would be dead right now.'

Goldilocks concentrated on her cocoa, while Mummy Bear hushed Daddy Bear, saying, 'Now's not the time, dear.'

'I'm so sorry,' Goldilocks repeated. 'And to make up for it, I can promote this place to my followers. I've got *lots* of them, and when I show them pics and say what absolute darlings you all are, they'll come here and spend *heaps* of money.'

This didn't provoke exactly the reaction she had anticipated. The bears just seemed to ignore her, and continued to make encouraging noises about her getting on her way, clearly desperate to have her out of their fur.

They waved at her from the front door and pointed her in the direction of the road. Then, once she was definitely gone, they set off to find some dry wood for the fire so they could cook some more porridge.

'Did she think we ran a B & B?' Mummy Bear asked. 'Where did she think *we* slept?'

'And what was all that stuff about followers?' said Daddy Bear, disturbed. 'It was like she was pretending to be a business guru. Or a spiritual leader.' He couldn't tell which one he found less likely.

'She certainly seemed to think that her job was just to go around having opinions about things,' said Mummy Bear. 'Sad, really.'

As they walked and chatted, Mummy Bear suddenly had an idea.

'You know,' she said. 'We really *should* set up a B & B . . .'

A few days passed, during which the only excitement in the forest was when Kevin shared the video 'porridge thief lady' and it went viral.

A few days later there was a knock on the front door. Mummy Bear expected it to be a reporter who had seen the video and was after the bears' side of the story. Instead, she saw a group of five rather posh-looking young people, brimming with excitement.

'Can you squeeze us in?' one of them asked. 'We're sorry we didn't book, but we'd be totes gratef . . .'

It was lucky she had answered the door, and not Daddy Bear, who would have simply roared and showed his teeth.

'Come in,' Mummy Bear said, ushering them inside. And, when she asked them to explain, they showed her Goldilocks's Impsta posts.

It turned out Goldie wasn't quite as away-with-the-humans as the bears had thought. She had indeed given their 'B & B' an extremely generous plug. She went super-detailed on the amazing range of flavours in the three porridges she had tried.

One (which she called 'The Daddy Bear') she described as being savoury, flavoured with miso, soy sauce, bonito flakes, sesame oil, a dash of chilli and some peanuts for crunch. The second . . . Well, she described them all, is what I'm saying.

She also made special mention of the wide range of bed softness, which she thought an especially considerate touch. Finally, noting the charming setting and accessibility from the main road, she tipped it as her 'place to visit' of the year.

And, boy, were the Gold Diggers listening. From that moment on they came to visit in droves, with cash in hand.

By the following week Mummy Bear was kept busy all day every day serving the somewhat drippy hipsters who poured in a continuous drizzle from the highway.

Meanwhile, Daddy Bear and Kevin were occupied with saws and hammers out back, building an extension.

Strangely, far from impairing the success of the B & B, Daddy Bear's gruffness towards the guests soon became its key feature. Customers were always asking him to stop what he was doing so they could get a selfie with him, and he'd begrudgingly oblige, brushing the sawdust off his arms. His expressions, which ranged from stiff awkwardness to carnivorous anger, soon became Impsta-famous.

Over time, he came to feel affection for these odd, loud, brightly coloured young people who were so in awe of things that seemed entirely straightforward to him. They claimed to be 'obsessed' with the 'vintage' crockery and the 'retro' non-oat dairy milk on offer. Every now and then, one of them would strut over in their skin-tight jeans to show Daddy Bear the tattoo they'd had done of him.

When the bears' relatives came to visit, they would gaze around the place and marvel. At the impressive new decor; at the carving of the B & B's name above the fireplace in a clean sans-serif font, within the logo of a steaming bowl of porridge; at the sticker for Ogre Eats on the door.

And the relatives would look quizzically at the bears and ask, 'What is this all about?'

But the bears, who were settling into their newfound popularity, would pretend not to understand the question. All that mattered was that these pleasant young people trusted Goldie's opinion. And thanks to this, the numerous stumbling blocks for low-income bears trying to start their own businesses had disappeared. But rather than explain all this, they would just smile and shrug.

Meanwhile, their business continued to thrive.

(And the Wi-Fi password, if you want to know, was 'goldilox' – all lower case.)

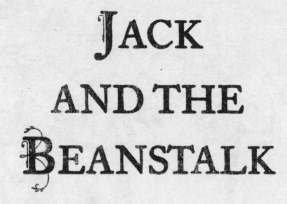

JACK
AND THE
BEANSTALK

*Jack was keen to implement a more disruptive start-up
culture as he pivoted from cow to beans.*

Jack was a teenage boy who lived with his grandmother in a small, tumbledown shack. Besides this miserable dwelling (which in truth did a disservice to the term 'shack') they owned the tiny strip of land next to it, and one starving cow.

They lived a hard and a hungry life, working every hour god sent just to keep hold of their meagre possessions. Local businesses (primarily the King Burger scrag-offal factory) offered only zero-hours contracts and no benefits. The concept of a living wage was but a distant memory, and in this poorest district of Albion even a lad as optimistic as Jack had to concede there were no prospects. *Albion* – once a rich and proud nation, a boastful capital of empire, now a neglected and unlovely backwater.

Jack was an intense and earnest youth, for which his grandmother loved him, but she wished he'd be more realistic. Every day he was out running errands for the local tailor and the local butcher, and he would have done the same for the local candlestick maker if the economy still supported such a thing. He insisted on not working for the 'big tax-exempt conglomerates' as he called them. But they owned everything now.

As a consequence, their savings were practically down to zero.

'Why don't you go into search engine optimization like all the other kids?' Jack's grandmother asked.

'Gran!' he said, with a look of horror that shamed her. 'I would never allow my horizons to be confined to such a . . . such a constricted, *narrow* existence. Making money for those faceless behemoths. Assisting in their domination and destruction of the ordinary worker and her or his rights. Once you go down that path, the next thing you know you're fifty, and *dead.*'

His grandmother, who was eighty and at least half alive, wanted to object. The way she saw it, everyone had to do jobs they didn't want to do in order to make ends meet. In her day, that was what you did to survive. She had, over the years, been a scullery maid, a street sweeper, a coal miner and a prostitute – sometimes all in the course of the same weekend. But Jack insisted on only doing jobs that were part of his quote unquote *journey.*

She supposed he was right. Even though letting him pursue his goals in such a fashion made it harder for them to eat in the short term, she trusted it would lead to something better in the long – for the two of them, hopefully, rather than just for the planet. So she wearily acquiesced, which was how conversations with Jack always ended, since he was so adamantly fixed to his own point of view.

'And, while we're about it,' Jack said, 'I think it's time we sold Cow Slave.'

His grandmother sighed, more wearily than ever. She

had known this day would come. 'I wish you'd let me call her something nice,' she said sadly. 'Like Hilda, or Primrose.'

'Giving a human name to an animal you enslave is *profoundly* disrespectful,' said Jack with an air that made Gran suspect there was a new lecture he had been cooking up and that he was eager to unburden himself. She backed down as fast as she could.

'Why sell her, though?' Gran asked. 'She's the last thing we've got!'

'Renewable resources,' Jack said.

'I thought milk was a renewable resource,' mumbled Gran, and immediately kicked herself.

'So's the *methane* they burp!' Jack yelled. Then he stopped and looked down at his shoes. He hated it when he shouted at Gran. He let out a deep breath.

'Plant-based food,' he went on, much more quietly, 'is the future. Vegan produce is in ever-increasing demand. My first choice would be soya beans, although I'm not sure whether making tofu is possible, with old stockings, a rolling pin and a tin bath . . . I'm looking into crowdfunding.'

'Tofu?' Gran asked. Up until now this had only been a word to her. She had a vague notion that it was a sort of synthetic toffee from foreign parts.

Jack was only too pleased to enlighten her. He explained how tofu was healthier than meat, more respectful to the body, kinder to the planet. He couldn't help being passionate about it, and, as he went on, his voice rose. He reached a crescendo with the insistence, 'to continue eating dairy and red meat knowing the *true* consequences, especially when there is a perfectly viable alternative, isn't just suicide – it is *murder*!'

Cow Slave and Jack's grandmother had both retreated away from Jack across the yard during this speech.

'Sell her, then,' Gran said. 'Go on. See what you can get.'

And as Jack led Cow Slave down the street, her bell jangling softly, Gran leaned against the fence for a moment, mopping her brow and taking deep breaths of silence.

Unable to relax during daylight hours, Gran immediately set to work turning the earth on their scrawny patch of soil so it would be ready for sowing when Jack came back.

And before she knew it, there he was. He hadn't been gone nearly long enough to trade Cow Slave in for her skin, ligaments and cartilage at the King Burger factory, and then reinvest that money in some crops. Besides, he was smiling, which for some obscure reason made her feel threatened.

She peered past him, trying to see the bag of seed, but there wasn't one. 'Best get sowing, Jack,' she said. 'Quick as you can.'

'Here you go.' He held out his hand.

There was nothing in it, save for a few bits of pocket lint. Gran looked at him, confused.

'*Here*,' he insisted. He held his hand up closer, and Gran saw that there *was* something there, after all: three minuscule beans. She looked at him again. He was still grinning.

'Three beans,' she said.

'I got an incredible deal,' Jack said. 'The last three beans from a really special crop. A *magic* crop. This will change our lives!'

Even a grandmother's love could not soften this disappointment. She felt sour. 'What shall we call these?' she asked quietly. 'Bean slaves, I suppose.'

Jack looked a little crestfallen. He started to explain the benefits of 'the three-seed crop', but Gran had not the heart to listen. Once upon a time, it would have been perfectly acceptable – advisable, in fact – to box the young idiot's ears until he howled, to teach him a lesson. But one did not do such things nowadays. And besides – what lesson could he learn? They had nothing left to lose.

Instead, she slapped her grandson's hand aside, told him a couple of home truths in a level voice, and stalked away.

She went to lie on her bed, pulled the blanket up over her nose and stared at the ceiling.

At some point she must have fallen asleep, because before she knew it there was a gentle *tap-tap* at her bedroom door, and Jack was coming in with a cup of tea for her. Light shone through the windows, although not as much light as usual.

'Gran, darling,' Jack said. 'It's morning.'

She grunted. Before she'd fallen asleep, she had decided that she was never going to speak again, since no one ever listened to her anyway.

She sat up in bed and accepted the tea. It was flavoured with lemon, which she regarded as suspiciously flamboyant and continental, and only marginally better than no tea at all. She sipped it with a grimace, then noticed that Jack was smiling at her.

'Want to know what's happened?' he asked.

She didn't really. She grunted again.

Jack threw open the curtains, and Gran was confronted by a vision. Of what, she was not at first sure. It was green, and it filled the entire sky. Gradually, she made out what seemed to be leaves the size of boat-sails (not that she had seen those before, but as she pictured them from stories) and a tree trunk as wide as a boat. (She was not practised in the art of similes, rarely having recourse to them.)

Gran grunted, with slightly more upward inflection this time, in a way that was intended to express, *Who the living hell put that there?*

'You did,' said Jack, understanding her perfectly. 'It grew from one of the seeds!'

When Jack started to climb the thing in the garden, Gran repeatedly grunted at him to be careful. And he was, for her sake – until he was up out of sight. Then, he began leaping and clambering with abandon. After all, he reasoned, if he slipped his fall would be cushioned by hundreds of thick, billowy leaves.

He had never been so excited.

Two hours in, he had nearly reached the cloud canopy which perpetually covered this part of the world (we are talking about Albion, after all). Here he stopped for a rest, sitting on the edge of a leaf and eating the sandwiches he had made with the last scraps of bread in the kitchen.

It was incredible to look down on Albion from this far up. Beautiful in a way, but melancholy too, with its great abandoned castles, gloomy desolate towns and slums with smoke rising from them. Brushing breadcrumbs from his lap to the birds that circled far below, he got up and carried on, excited about what he might find.

Soon he was through to the other side of the cloud, his head peeping out.

When he saw what was up there, he yelped and fell off his leaf. Then he clambered back up for a second look. Before him was a majestic castle fashioned from blocks of stone, each as large as a boat. (Here, his grandmother's nurturing influence was evident.) The gates were open, and so Jack wandered in, looking cheerfully for someone to make friends with, oblivious to the sharp teeth of the portcullis dangling far above his head.

He stopped in the castle's courtyard and looked around. There was no one in sight. A rare glimmer of common sense told Jack not to shout out; instead he went in through a nearby entrance and down a series of high hallways, cautiously pushing open each of the colossal wooden doors and looking through. The third one opened into a dungeon where sparkled a large pile of some material that looked very valuable. Unless Jack was much mistaken, it was gold.

Then something next to the pile moved, making Jack jump.

A magical creature flapped its wings graciously, rising into the air, then settling down again. It looked like a gigantic goose, but with golden feathers. Beneath it, Jack glimpsed several golden eggs. What's more, the fluttering of its wings made a draught that stroked the strings of a nearby harp – *also*, if Jack's eyes were not mistaken, made of gold. Jack was transported for a moment by a heavenly arpeggio that sprang through the air.

He heard a loud squeak, and turned to find a shape looming over him.

'Sacré bleu,' said a sympathetic voice. 'Oh, quelle dommage! Another beanstalk refugee! The idea of you risking your life just to get here makes my blood run cold, you petit chéri!'

'Eh?' asked Jack, but before he could request any further explanation, or even get a good look at who he was talking to, he was scooped up by a large hand and dumped in what seemed to be the pocket of a giant apron. The being who had kidnapped him – who he got the sense was an enormous elderly woman – rushed forward and back along the corridors, muttering to herself nervously.

'What if he finds out,' she was saying to herself. 'He détestes them so much, these foreigners, these beanstalk interlopers. He bites their heads off and chews them up!'

'You mean others have been here before me?' Jack asked, sticking his head out of the pocket.

'Ah, oui,' replied the giantess. She went on to recount the complete history of the relationship between Albion and the land beyond the clouds. 'Hundreds of years ago, we were all part of the same continent. We were very close. But then – ah, un jour triste – Albion split away from the rest and was never the same. Now poor garçons like you risk your necks climbing beanstalks – all so you can have access to our wine, cheese and job market.'

'It's fascinating,' said Jack. 'And so sad, as well. I say, your English is pretty bloody impressive, you know?'

The old woman shrugged modestly and emitted a sound like an orgy between fourteen vowels. Then suddenly she tensed.

'Attend!' she whispered. 'Silencieux!'

From somewhere nearby came the forbidding *Boom! Boom! Boom!* of enormous footsteps. The sound made Jack's bones shake, and before he knew what was what the giantess had plucked him from her pocket and thrown him bodily into a gigantic pot of flour. Jack spluttered and dusted the flour away from his mouth (noting, approvingly, that it was wholemeal, with chunks as big as his ear). It seemed the giantess had carried him all the way to the castle's kitchen.

The booming footsteps reached the kitchen, and a cavernous voice intoned, 'Pastis. Quickly.'

'But I thought –' said the giantess.

'I said pastis, woman! And a selection of charcuterie and fromage. And bread, with pâté made from the liver of a bird that has been forced to eat pâté! Until it dies! And on top I want another of those birds that has been drowned in the finest Armagnac, while the chef reads aloud the poems of Baudelaire.'

'Our finest delicacy,' she said reverently. 'Bien sûr!'

This is a bit reductive, isn't it? Jack thought.

'Stop talking and fetch the déjeuner!' yelled the giant. 'I've been working all day, for almost two hours, with a long sleep either side. Is it too much to ask to have a few drinks and thirty filterless cigarettes while I watch black-and-white documentaries about the futility of existence?'

Jack, in his flour pot, felt his blood boil. Now, he knew that it wasn't OK to go to other countries and thrust your nose into situations you didn't fully understand yet, in order to 'save the day', but he also found this giant fellow's abusive attitude towards his wife inexcusable. What Jack was going to *do* about it, he wasn't yet sure.

Then he heard a distant sound like a steam train approaching through a tunnel.

'What *is* that,' the giant was muttering, and Jack realized that he was running his nose along all the pots on the kitchen shelf. He was sniffing them.

'FEEE-FIE-FOE-*FFUUURGHM*,' the giant murmured under his breath (which to Jack was loud enough to shiver his bones and loosen his bowels). 'I smell the blood of an *Englishman*,' the giant went on, almost meditatively. 'And, be he alive or be he dead, I'll grind his bones to make my bread!'

With a flourish, the giant pulled the lid from the flour pot.

If he had expected to find a terrified creature cowering inside, he was disappointed. Instead he saw Jack, up to his knees in flour and with his arms folded angrily.

'Where to start?' said Jack. 'First, the reason you are so aggressive is because you eat so much red meat. And bread made from ground bones? Your cholesterol must be sky-high. Ever heard of a balanced diet? It would make you healthier, happier, kinder, less of a burden on the health system, and more in tune with the world around you. You really need to practise some self-care.'

The giant blinked.

'Not to mention the quality of writing round here. It is *decidedly* substandard. You've said nothing but clichés since you appeared!'

'Englishman,' said the giant, narrowing his eyes.

'Your tone implies you consider that a pejorative,' Jack replied, 'which I object to. Even so, I should say that primarily I consider myself a citizen of the world.'

'*Englishman*,' the giant growled. He bared his teeth, each tall as a boat, and every one bleak and brown with filth.

'I should point out my mother was born in Wales,' Jack went on. 'And, I'm, er – well, as a matter of fact, I'm in the process of applying for an Irish passport.'

'ENGLISHMA–!' the giant roared. But his voice was cut short by a colossal thump like distant thunder.

The giant's eyes, which had never shown much intelligence to begin with, became utterly vacant. His head wavered a moment, then it slipped from Jack's view altogether, followed by a loud crash that overturned the flour pot, throwing Jack out on to the shelf. He peered over the edge, and saw on the ground far below him the body of the felled giant. Vast and unmoving as a range of hills.

Dusting himself off, Jack stood and looked up at the giantess, who was staring in wonder at the blood-smeared rolling pin in her hand.

'I've imagined doing that for decades,' she said, 'but I

never thought I'd have the courage. He was just so resistant to change.'

Jack beamed at her. 'I'm so proud of you,' he said.

The giantess was already dragging the body towards the cellar with a cleaver tucked under one arm when Jack had a thought.

'May I say,' Jack said, watching her. 'And it's none of my business, I know . . . but I believe some serious investment opportunities have just become available to you, and I'd like to help you with them.'

She stopped and dropped the body. 'I'm listening,' she said.

Jack and the giantess discussed business dealings late into the night, and he finally convinced her that a giant pile of gold wouldn't gain any value just sitting in a dungeon. She could, he suggested, allow him to transport her gold down the beanstalk and convert it into bitcoin. He would be able to manage her investment for what was to her an extremely modest fee, and was to Jack and Gran a multiple of their entire life earnings. Then, if this turned out mutually beneficial, they might discuss the sale of golden eggs as well as lucrative recordings and perhaps public appearances of the golden harp. She agreed to it all.

So, the next morning, he climbed back down the beanstalk.

When Jack's grandmother saw him appear with a sack full of pure gold slung over one shoulder, she grunted. It's hard to put into words exactly what this grunt expressed – it contained astonishment at her grandson's skill and bravado, and also a grudging admission that perhaps he understood at least a little bit about how to get ahead these days. Possibly also an unavoidable twinge of jealousy that magic beans hadn't been on the market when her husband was Jack's age, sixty years ago.

And it wasn't just Jack, Gran and the giantess who prospered. Over the following years, *everybody* benefitted from the improved relationship between those at the top of the beanstalk and those at the bottom. The giantess invested her new-found wealth in formerly depressed communities, primarily (thanks to her new friend) in plant-based foods. Not just in agriculture, but in research too. Soon, beanstalks could be seen throughout the land (despite some conservative-minded folk who decried them as aesthetic carbuncles), and were made safe for all to travel on. People transitioned to a largely meat-free diet. Methane levels fell, which unexpectedly made the air above the clouds much more pleasant.

Gradually, people stopped seeing beanstalks as a barrier at all. Movement was free and easy. Above and below the cloud there was a sense of shared identity and culture. Jack's generation came to refer to themselves as Beanstalkers.

When the giantess faced her final days, Jack ensured that she received the highest standard of end-of-life care available. After she passed on, Jack, as her executor, oversaw the conversion of the castle into affordable, accessible and comfortable accommodation for elderly giants. What remained of the giantess's fortune was then invested in a host of new green technologies, which would fund the National Health Service for a generation.

One morning, when that generation had grown wealthy and old and small-minded, Jack (who had been working hard and not paying attention to the news) woke up to discover that all beanstalks had been severed. Jack had no way to get back and manage the finances that were supposed to be pouring into Albion.

On every street there were signs outside houses and placards in people's hands, bearing the legend BEANSTEXIT MEANS BEANSTEXIT.

Despite being ungainly, stupid and meaningless, the phrase caught on. Jack heard it everywhere. Because his centre of operations was above the clouds, he was cut off from his meagre stipend just as the NHS was from its stupendous one. There were riots, and smoke in the street. Jack had to sell his house to settle his debts, and he ended up living in his gran's old shack with his granddaughter, who had no job.

'Grandad,' she said. 'How shall we eat?'

'I'm afraid,' he replied, 'the only thing we can do is buy a cow.'

'*Buy* a cow?' she said. It was the sort of thing people only did in history books. 'What should we call it?' she asked.

Jack regarded her sadly as he began to think of an answer.

GRETEL
AND
HANSEL

'This "Death by Chocolate" on the menu – I trust
it contains no gluten, dairy or sugar?'

It was around the third anniversary of their mother's passing that Gretel and Hansel's father returned to their shack with some exciting news.

'I've met someone,' he said. 'Someone very special. I'd like you to meet her too.'

'WTF,' said Gretel.

'Darling, please,' said their father. 'Be nice. I want you all to be friends.'

A shape appeared in the doorway, and the two children flinched. Stepmothers in this part of the world had a bit of a *reputation*. Boil you alive or feed you a poisoned apple as soon as look at you.

So the children stared until the silhouette resolved itself into a woman. Their father's new paramour looked to be in her mid thirties, and was rather pretty (in an obvious sort of way, Gretel thought), with blonde hair, hoop earrings and lots of make-up. 'You poor little *darlings*,' she said, gathering them in a hug and pressing their faces to her chest. 'You must miss having a mother so much.'

Gretel and Hansel's mother had brought them up to be nice to strangers, but the sudden horror that *this* stranger was to be their new mother bypassed their finer impulses.

'Who the eff are *you*?' said Gretel.

Hansel burst into tears.

'Oh! It's an awful shock, springing something like this on you,' the woman said. 'If we're going to be friends why don't we all go out for some nice food?'

G and H slumped back on the sofa, one sobbing, the other sullenly quiet and staring. Meanwhile this strange woman stood over them, radiating unsolicited sympathy.

The children's father, who was such a little twerp he doesn't even get a name, watched anxiously. He was anxious both by nature and by learning – it was difficult to hold down a job in the Inquisition as long as he had without feeling moderately tense at all times. For starters, there was the atmosphere of the place. Gloomy. Grim. Not to say, well, *depressing*.

It was desperately difficult to attract people to work in the palace at all. And once you did get them there, to make them stay.

As the recently promoted head of human resources, he knew this well. His boss insisted that the Inquisition had a diversity problem. But this was the one topic on which he allowed himself to openly disagree. The Inquisition united people of every race, sexuality, gender and creed: they all wanted not to do it.

You could post flyers on trees and in tavern windows all across the realm, and word them as positively as you could – *ENTHUSIASTIC, SELF-MOTIVATED TEAM PLAYER WANTED* and so forth – but it was always the same sallow, back-stabbing malcontents that came forward. He had a dream of a cheerful Inquisition of contented employees who had good relationships with their line managers. But it seemed further away than ever.

Part of the problem was, of course, the reputation of his assistant, Gorbo the Bludger. A man who preferred to sever limbs first and refuse to answer questions later. No matter how many sensitivity training sessions you sent him on, his attitude to conflict resolution remained totally cut and dried. Or, chopped and mopped.

And then there was this new edict about inclusivity, which required a certain number of the department's staff to be women. In desperation he had been forced to go out and actively search for women willing to work at the Inquisition. At first, the willingness proved elusive, but once Gorbo had indulged in a few dozen light dunkings and burnings, the message got across.

In fact, it was on one of these recruitment drives that the children's father had met Jaimee.

Ah, Jaimee. Light of his life.

'A big personality' she'd called herself when he'd first met her. 'People either love me or they hate me,' she'd said.

And, boy, did they.

Jaimee was an absolute riot, always one to point at the sundial the moment five thirty came and say it was 'wine o'clock'. Always one who, when everyone else had gone home, insisted on ordering another bottle of 'vino del collapso', or suffered the next morning from 'wine flu'. Ah, she *got* him.

She and the children would see eye to eye. He was sure of it.

It would just take a little time.

Gretel and Hansel, for their part, were not so sure.

Their new stepmother spent a lot of her time in the bath. Either there or laughing nasally at the antics of her favourite personalities on *Love Archipelago*, a series that had seen an enormous ratings bump after it changed its title from its original incarnation, *Hate Cove*.

'She doesn't even watch *Queer Eye for the Straight Squire*,' muttered Gretel. 'And that's actually good.'

Jaimee also vaped a lot, and when they accused her of it, she pretended she hadn't been. Despite the fact the whole house smelled like strawberry cheesecake or banoffee pie. The children would have genuinely preferred the smell of tobacco smoke.

Worst of all, however, was the food. Most days, Jaimee either came home with takeaways for the kids from King Burger (where her new husband at least got a discount) or flopped on the sofa and ordered in from Ogre Eats. Everything that wasn't a burger or fried was full of sugar.

This was a treat the first night. The second night, it was still a treat. Maybe more so. But by the fourth night, they felt ill at the thought of fried food, and three weeks later, Gretel and Hansel were starting seriously to worry about their health. They felt bloated, light-headed and sometimes short of breath. Also they had less energy, and felt lazy and unambitious. Just like those kids in all the stories, who ended up killed by their stepmothers, too addled to run away or think their way out of the situation.

This all became terribly apparent one day when they opened the kitchen cupboard to see all the rice and lentils and preserved foods had been thrown away to be replaced with sugary breakfast cereals, chocolate and crisps.

'Now's the time to act,' whispered Gretel. 'If we leave it any longer it'll be too late. We have to go out and forage for healthy food.'

Hansel agreed. 'While we've still got the energy to move,' he said.

'You little sweeties getting on OK?' asked their stepmother.

They both jumped and turned to find her leaning in the kitchen doorway, smiling at them. 'I was thinking of ordering Blando's. Who's up for that?'

Blando was the name of an extremely successful entrepreneur who sold grilled meats and chipped potatoes all over the realm, but in the environs of whose inns a suspicious number of donkeys had gone missing. Impossible as it seemed, some people *liked* going to Blando's, and even boasted of it like a badge of pride. It really was something the health-conscious twins found too appalling to imagine.

They screamed and ran out of the room.

'Smashing,' said Jaimee, taking this as an expression of approval. 'I'll get ordering then . . .'

'Just a bit further,' said Hansel. 'There should be nuts and fruits aplenty around here.'

'Are you *sure* we'll be able to find our way home?' said Gretel, looking back in the direction they'd come from.

'Of course,' said Hansel. 'I've left a very careful trail of twigs to show us the way.'

'But there are twigs on the ground anyway,' said Gretel.

'Ah, of course,' said Hansel, nodding to himself. 'I forgot it might not be so easy for everyone to understand. You see, I gather my own twigs, and lay them carefully, one every three paces, so that the trail of them leads back in the direction we have come from. See? Clever, isn't it?' Then he chuckled in disbelief. 'Honestly, Gretel, sometimes I wonder if your head's screwed on properly!'

Gretel just stared at him.

Detecting he had done something wrong, Hansel wandered off and decided to prove his point by following his sticks back a little way. After six paces he lost the trail, and after searching around fruitlessly for a while, just stood there swearing.

Gretel sighed. He had *promised* she could leave the directions to him. Had demanded to take charge of them, in fact. And now they were lost.

'It seems to *me*,' said Hansel, who didn't like being sighed at, 'that these days men get criticized for trying to do anything. By others who are oh-so happy to stand around blaming and complaining instead of helping.'

But Gretel wasn't paying any attention. She was advancing towards a little cottage that had appeared in a clearing up ahead. It was small and pretty, but there was something odd about it. Something Gretel couldn't put her finger on . . .

Hansel followed on behind her. As they got closer they began to feel unaccountably hungry.

When they were standing next to the cottage, Hansel reached out a finger and scooped out some of the mortar between the bricks. It was some sort of gooey mixture. He tasted it.

'Omigod,' he said.

So Gretel reached out and snapped a piece off the roof. Her saliva glands running like a tap, she dipped it in the mortar, then crunched it between her teeth.

'Omi*god*,' she said.

The mortar was smashed avocado. The roof was sourdough toast.

It was delicious.

Gretel looked at her brother, then in unison they began to devour the little house's guttering, which was fashioned from endive leaves lightly dressed with a piquant vinaigrette. As they ate, they moved inside the house and stared around in wonder. At the walls, fashioned from falafel and quinoa bricks. At the ceiling, made from an interlocking pattern of keto-friendly summer rolls, each bursting with fresh ingredients.

They devoured them, one after the other.

Then they lay on their backs, dreamy smiles on their faces, groaning.

'We have *got* to tell Goldilocks about this place,' said Gretel.

It was the last thing either of them said before they fell into a food coma.

*

'Time to wake up, my dears,' said a voice.

Hansel started awake and looked around. They were still in the cottage, but their situation was not quite as rosy as before. Gretel was pressing at the bars of a cage surrounding her. They were firm – and most definitely inedible.

'Dafuq,' she said.

'Indeed,' replied the woman who had spoken. 'You will soon learn why you have been put in a cage. Your brother here is going to help me look after you.'

Gretel found this to be profoundly problematic on a number of levels. So much so, in fact, that she refrained from responding immediately, in order to give herself time to properly formulate a reply that would do justice to this outrage. But before she could do that, Hansel jumped in.

'Er . . . let her go?' he said.

The woman sized them both up. 'Hmm. It would seem that you've both been eating a very unhealthy diet recently,' she said. 'And it's my mission to make children as healthy as can be. No matter how harsh the method! Some people might consider me an extremist. Far from it – it is *they* who are the extremists, for trying to stop me! How I HATE them!'

Hansel frowned, trying to follow this train of thought.

'Fat children make me *so unhappy*,' said the woman. 'I can't stand seeing them like that, so miserable. I want everyone to be as happy as I am!'

'You don't look happy,' said Gretel.

'Well, I *am*. I'm deliriously happy. See?' She stretched her face into an awful rictus. 'HAHAHAHAHA!'

The children cowered beneath her.

'I love life,' she went on, 'and I live a very full one. I do yoga and parkrun, and I have activated cashew nuts and apple cider vinegar for breakfast. But I believe in balance so I allow myself a weekly cheat day, when I eat an orange. I think it's tremendously blinkered to imagine we all have to fit into stereotypical heteronormative roles in this day and age. The idea we need to be in a relationship to be happy, for instance, is grotesquely outdated.'

'She's been dumped,' said Gretel.

'I have *not*,' said the woman.

There was an awkward silence.

'It was mutual,' she said. 'Besides, I'm better off without him. He had a total dad bod, which – despite what some people might say – was disgusting. Not that he has it any more, ha.'

'Oh no?' Hansel asked, not really liking where this was going.

'No. Well.' The woman looked coy. 'I turned him into a hamster, didn't I?'

Hansel snapped his fingers in recognition. Finally all the pieces fell into place. The small, mysterious cottage alone in the centre of the forest. The mad crone in a witch's hat. The badge on her chest which proclaimed a four-broomstick rating from *Which? Witch* magazine.

'I think she might be a witch,' he whispered to Gretel.

Gretel stared back at him with loathing.

'Really, I'm actually very grateful to him!' the witch went on. 'Seeing that flolloping tummy of his around every day helped me realize that sugar is the enemy. I've now completely eradicated it from my diet, and my life's work is to help others – children specifically – to stop eating sugar. Entirely. *Forever.*'

Even though the very purpose of the children's woodland excursion had been to gain access to a healthier diet, the witch's speech made for pretty dismal listening.

'Without sugar, your heart is healthier,' said Witchy. 'Your skin is clearer. You lose fat. Your bones are stronger and your blood is healthier. And you are more delicious.'

'Come again?' asked Hansel.

'More delicious,' the witch repeated.

That was what Hansel thought she'd said.

'Delicious in what sense?' asked Hansel.

'In the cooked and eaten by me sense,' said the witch.

Gretel stirred uncomfortably, noticed a clicking noise, and looked down. What she had thought were twigs scattered across the floor beneath her were, she now saw, a carpet of discarded bones and human skulls.

'Right,' said Hansel. 'Good to clear that up.'

From that moment on, Hansel focused on talking to the woman as much as possible. Partly to elicit any information he could that would help his sister escape, partly to understand her somewhat hard-to-defend motives, but mostly because when you're chatting it's hard to kill, butcher, cook and eat a child. At least Hansel expected that it probably was. After all, everyone likes being asked about their work.

'It's terrible that, in this day and age, parents allow their offspring to get so unhealthy,' the witch said. 'So, I've developed a range of health-food protein shakes to fit in with the fast-moving modern forest lifestyle. Look, I've got my own branding.'

She pointed to a nearby stand, fully stocked with brightly coloured cartons. Hansel picked one up, and felt its contents slosh around inside. He looked at the copy on the back.

'*HI!*' it said. '*I'm packed to the brim with minerals, proteins and healthy bacteria, to make me a truly world-beating drink-style accessory that will sustain you throughout the day. Whether you're going for that all-out session at the gym, getting those pesky packed lunches together for the little ones, or just kicking back and enjoying some well-earned You Time, I'm the ideal treat. Oh, and did I mention I **taste great too**!?*' Hansel rubbed the space between his eyebrows to alleviate a sharp pain that had sprung up there. '*I've been prepared with care and passion by a team who just LOVE making smoothies – in the office we like to refer to ourselves as SMOOTH operators lol (except for Karen who says we're a bunch of smug c–*'

Hansel replaced the carton on the shelf. There were, he noted, several different flavours.

'All natural packaging,' said the witch. 'Fully biodegradable. That load of crap on the back is all made up of course, but you have to have it these days. And the trick with branding is to remember that your logo has to be so obvious that it's still recognizable even when it's just a tiny tile icon on someone's phone.'

'Yeah, yeah, everyone knows that. What's in this?' Hansel said, holding up a bottle labelled TURMERIC AWAKENING.

'Tamara Fortescue,' said the woman. 'From the gated

community at the top of the hill. Plus, you know, kale and carrot and whatever.'

'From a gated community to a grated community,' said Hansel, solemnly replacing the bottle on the shelf.

'But the problem at the moment is not enough flavour. Despite what the copy says. Fat girl, see? I want to start a new range based on leaner kids, like your sister. Very exciting to have found her. If this range is a hit, I want to move into appetite-supressing lollipops for children. Another good marketing deal is to have your own awareness campaign, named from a pun on a month's name. Like Veganuary. But I can't settle on a name. I was thinking of Eatchildtober.'

'It's a bit clunky,' said Hansel. 'How about Dismember?'

The witch's face lit up. 'I like it,' she said. She looked at him shrewdly. 'You're clearly one to watch.'

During this exchange, Hansel's eye roved around the cottage, which was surprisingly capacious when you were inside.

'Why is there a standing desk in here?'

'That's Darren's,' said the witch. 'This is a shared workspace. He only works Weds to Fri. He's a tidiness consultant.'

'Does he not mind children coming and eating parts of the office?' Hansel asked.

'Not if I magic it back each night,' she snapped.

'I think this is mightily impressive, what you've done here,' he said. 'Starting from scratch, taking your own business idea and really making it work for you and your community.'

This rather took the witch by surprise. She'd been expecting a little pushback from him on the whole chopping-up-and-eating-his-sister issue, but this young man really seemed to have a mature perspective on things.

'I'm glad you see it that way,' she said.

'How could I not,' said Hansel. 'You've found a gap in the marketplace, and you're exploiting it, benefitting the forest as a whole. What's more, your product is locally sourced, and it's *green*.'

'Well, I don't really know how to respond to compliments,' said the witch. 'But nevertheless I am rather touched. Thank you.'

'Not at all,' said Hansel. He had been going to go on and say that surely some sort of medal of achievement was in order, or nomination for businesswitch of the year. But he didn't want to overspinach the smoothie.

'How do you manage to make these wonderful drinks, anyway?' he said.

'Glad you asked,' said the witch, pulling back a hessian tarpaulin to reveal a giant machine.

Hansel stared up at it in unfeigned wonder. It stood six feet tall and consisted of a giant glass bowl with a mechanism at the bottom boasting a pair of hellish-looking blades.

'State-of-the-art blender,' said the witch nonchalantly. 'Got it off the dark web. Ex-military. You can't even buy these things.'

'How does it work?' Hansel asked, briefly wondering what the christing hell it was that the military were blending and why.

'Best I show you, since it will be your job,' she said. 'First you set the ladder firmly against it, like so. Then, you put the chopped-up meat and other ingredients in at the top here.'

'I'm not sure I could reach,' said Hansel.

'Course you could!' she insisted. 'You just clamber right on to the rim like this, you see, and, using a stick, you press the ingredients down so that they properly mix.'

'Show me how to use the stick?' said Hansel, his heart beating fast.

'You lean in like this,' said the witch, her voice echoing from within the bowl.

'Ah, got it,' said Hansel, giving her a thumbs up as he kicked away the ladder. 'And then I assume that you switch it on with this lever here.'

The woman was still nodding, thinking what a quick boy he was on the uptake, as the machine made a roaring sound and she disappeared into a blur.

There are authors, no doubt, capable of transforming into cool syllables the howl that rose up as the blades reduced her into a thousand gory slivers. But dear reader, I am not among them.

The lid not being on the blender, the resultant mess was quite considerable and covered Hansel from head to foot. Even his sister in her cage did not escape a coating.

In short order, Hansel had smashed the lock with a stone and freed her. Moments later, they were both trotting back down the hill in roughly the direction they'd come from, and trying not to think about what Darren's reaction would be when he came into work the next morning.

They found their way home in the end thanks to stumbling upon one of the bike route trails that had been marked through the forest under the directions of the mayor of Fairyland, to offer green belt access to residents of the suburbs. Therefore their journey home had no dangers other than having to dive out of the way of cyclists self-importantly bombing it along.

Their father and stepmother were, of course, out of their minds with worry, and so grateful to have the kids back that they overlooked the foolishness of their setting out on so dangerous an expedition. The children in turn detailed their concerns about the family's diet, while their parents listened with due seriousness. They would all take turns to make dinner from now on, with perhaps the occasional takeaway on Fridays, as a treat. And so they lived, healthy and happy together.

That is, until six months later, when they all caught the plague and died.

THE
THREE
NANNY
GOATS GRUFF

'All I'm saying is, as well as being a goat,
coincidentally I am also the G.O.A.T.'

Once, there were three nanny goats who needed to get to the other side of a stream, where there was a meadow with plenty of fresh grass. To get there, they had to cross a bridge, but this particular bridge had such a fearsome reputation that the other goats didn't dare to cross it. For legend had it that beneath the bridge dwelled a troll.

The grass on the near side of the bridge was short and stubby, thinned out by overconsumption and bleached pale by the sun. The grass on the other side, however, looked lush, verdant, springy. The stuff of a goat's dreams. This, the goats reflected, seemed always to be the way. 'Someone ought to coin a phrase about it,' they said.

'I've heard it's an optical illusion,' said the youngest of the three goats. 'Your eyes see grass at a side angle when looking from far away, but when you look down from above you're seeing a different part of the plant. And it actually *is* slightly less green. You know? I think I heard that on a podcast.'

'How interesting,' said the second goat. 'I've never quite worked out how to listen to podcasts. Maybe you could show me later . . .'

'Girls,' said the third goat, 'we're prevaricating. Let's get on with this.'

The two older sisters encouraged the youngest to go first. She was frightened, but they knew that getting over the bridge would boost her confidence. Plus, then she'd get the pick of the delicious grass on the other side as a reward.

'There you go,' said the second goat, as her younger sister stepped forward.

'You're practically across it already!' said the eldest.

The youngest goat was called Gruff, which was a perfectly good name for a goat. She usually hated the name, but right now it made her feel bigger and braver than she really was. She couldn't deny that her legs were shaking and, as she peered down through the large gaps between the planks, she hoped that trolls slept during the daytime. Or that the one who purportedly lived under this bridge might be away on holiday.

The stream was particularly fast and deep as it ran beneath the bridge, and Gruff thought she sensed something stirring in the dark, cool shadows below. But she steeled herself to keep moving. To her ears, each of her footsteps made an incredibly loud, echoing clatter on the wood.

'Keep going!' said her eldest sister. 'You can do it!'

'Oi!' said a deep voice. 'Make me a sandwich!'

'What?' said Gruff, coming to a stop.

'A sandwich or get your udders out.' The voice sounded bored and dismissive, and yet the youngest goat also sensed that it was intently focused upon her.

'I don't really know –'

'Udders or get off the bridge.'

'I don't know what you mean,' said the goat, hating the tremor that had come into her voice.

'*I don't know what you mean*,' mocked the voice. 'Are you CRYING? How did a baby get on to this bridge all by herself?'

The goat's two older sisters were shouting, urging her on. 'Go on, you're almost over the other side!'

But she didn't hear them. She was in the grip of the voice's owner. 'What *are* you?' she asked. 'What do you *want*?'

'I'd say kill yourself, but you'd probably get that wrong. End up a vegetable. Not that anyone would notice. If you had any personality, you'd be a feminazi, but you're just a crybaby. I hope your favourite maiden aunt gets cancer.'

This was too much. It was so horribly offensive that it shocked Gruff back to reality for a second. Surely no one could know her well enough to hate her this much. She heard the voices of her sisters yelling encouragement, and she bounded off the bridge.

She had made it! Safe on the other side, she turned to watch her sisters follow her.

The next goat stepped on to the bridge. She was heavier, and the boards creaked a bit underneath her.

'Ugh,' said the voice. 'Look at you, you ugly virgin.'

Now, this isn't a very nice thing to say to anyone, but it struck home with unerring accuracy. The second goat stood stock-still, quivering.

At this point I should mention that the second goat's name was also Gruff. As stated above, a perfectly normal name for a goat. There are goats called Gruff all over the place – you can't throw a pebble in the Scottish Highlands (should you want to do so) without hitting one. However, naming *two* daughters Gruff does put a bit of a question mark over the parents for me. Whether they were playing a prank or simply inattentive, we'll never know. Anyway. It's just a thing to mention in passing. Back to the tale.

'That's none of your business,' said middle sister Gruff. 'Don't be so rude.'

'Oh, it's *me* who's being rude? When you're the one waddling your fat arse across my bridge, smashing it to pieces with your clumsy hooves and making it stink of stupid, ugly virgins?'

So awful was this that Gruff burst into tears. She had, as a matter of fact, just been through a nasty breakup with a frankly shallow young ram from the other side of the mountain who'd had completely unrealistic body expectations (brought about, no doubt, by an overexposure to EwePorn).

The third sister was *not* going to stand by and allow this to happen. 'KEEP GOING!' she bellowed.

'Come on, Gruff!' insisted the youngest sister.

Together, her sisters' voices pierced Gruff's indecision and gave her the bravery to act. Transforming the anger and hurt into physical energy, she reached the other side in three bounds. Her younger sister grabbed her in a hug and told her how brave she was.

'Woah!' came the voice from down in the trench. 'I'll send you an invoice for the damage, you tonne of lard!'

But then his voice was arrested by a new sound from above. Now the bridge really *did* groan. A huge shadow moved across it towards the centre. Boards squeaked, dust and crumbs and splinters spattered down into the shadows.

There were a few noises as the owner of the voice made as if to speak. A smacking of the lips. A clearing of the throat. A quiet chuckle as though in response to some wicked thought. But he said nothing.

The third goat stood there in the centre of the bridge. She bent her head and scrutinized the gaps between the boards. Her eyes flicked left and right, and she thought she spotted a movement. Now it was *she* who smacked *her* lips.

At this juncture I ought to point out that the third goat's name was *also* Gruff. Which, by any stretch of the imagination, is a demented name to give to three children. Literally WTF. By the time all three of them reached physical maturity, they would be impossible to tell apart. And I know what you're thinking: surely Gruff was their surname? No. Their surname was Yoshimoto. What a world. But, on with the story.

'Do you want to talk?' asked the third and eldest goat.

The thing in the gulch below responded to this with a tirade of invective, touching on many of the topics previously mentioned along with some new ones.

'I think you do want to talk,' the third goat said when he had finished.

The voice responded with an even louder and more unpleasant burst of abuse, this time focusing exclusively on the goat's tremendous size. In this, however, he erred. You see, she was very fond of her body and comfortable in it. It gave her a physical presence that she enjoyed, and lots of males (she happened to like males) really went for girls her size and made her feel decidedly special.

Plus, if her career as a professional counsellor had taught her anything, it was to combat aggression with kindness. She dealt with this sort of thing every day. And, right on cue, the guy seemed to be running out of energy.

'Perhaps I'm wrong,' she said, 'but I imagine you don't really like being down there. It must be dreadfully cold and damp.'

He tried to say a few things all at once, then fell silent. Nobody had ever stood up to him before.

'I also don't think you really mean the things that you say to people who cross this bridge,' she went on. 'I think it might be because someone said horrible things like that to you once. And you didn't like it. Which is goat nature. It must have been horrible for you.'

The silence under the bridge deepened.

'If I could speak to the person who hurt you, do you know what I would say? I'd say, "That's not fair. You're being horrible to someone who doesn't deserve it. Who *is* a good person, inside. He deserves to be treated nicely." Now, I wonder what *you* would say to them. Would it be the same as me?'

There was quietness below. Gruff waited. And then, just as she was about to go on, she heard the voice (much quieter this time) say, 'Yes.'

'Of course. You only say such horrible things to people up here on this bridge because you can't see their faces.

From where you're hidden down there in the dark, they're not real people to you. And do you know who I think you are *really* talking to when you say those things?'

There was another thoughtful silence. 'Myself?'

'Yes!' Gruff said. She smiled broadly. 'You've got it. You *are* clever. And, if you could confront the person who treated you badly, do you know what I think would be the best thing you could do for your own personal well-being?'

'I think so . . .' said the voice tentatively.

'Go on,' she said soothingly. 'You can say it.'

'Stamp on his balls?'

'Not quite.' She slapped away some flies with her tail. 'I was thinking of something else.'

'Oh . . .' Another pause. Then, 'Um . . . Forgive them?'

'That's it! Can I tell you something? I've never met anyone who's made such quick progress after just a few questions. I bet you're the cleverest clogs on the whole mountain. Why don't you come up so we can say hello?'

'Promise you won't do anything nasty? Like stamp on m–'

'We won't do *anything* nasty,' said the youngest sister.

'Come on out!' said the middle sister. 'There's some lovely grass up here. If that's your tipple.'

From the darkness under the bridge there emerged a very pale male goat. He blinked repeatedly in the sunlight, and seemed ashamed of his scrawny body.

The three goats Gruff (quelling their natural anger towards him with considerable effort) all welcomed him with a cheer. They were secretly amazed to find him so small, and wondered what had made his voice seem so deep and powerful – perhaps the echoing space beneath the bridge.

He shyly came over to them, and they all sniffed each other's arseholes (or whatever goats do to say hello), then set about having a good old grass lunch and a chinwag.

From that day on, they all got along famously.

The goat who had dwelled under the bridge (whose name, thank baby Jesus, was not Gruff) went off in search of other beings under bridges who were acting in the same way he had. Be they goats or otherwise, and no matter how terribly they were feared by the local populace, he mostly found them to be unloved, lost souls like himself who responded well to empathetic treatment and repented of their abusive behaviour, eventually becoming valued members of their communities.

Except for a few, who were just pricks. And those ones, he stamped on their balls.

THE 'UGLY' DUCKLING

Around these parts, asking if a bird was 'pond-body ready'
was considered offensive.

Once upon a time, a mother duck laid a clutch of eggs. When they hatched, she counted her ducklings, beaming with happiness and pride. Each was more gorgeous and adorable than the last.

Then, she reached the final duckling. This one was different from the others. Where the other ducklings were fluffy and yellow, this one was gangly and grey. Someone who cared about such things, and liked to put labels on them, might have described the last little duckling as ugly.

However, the mother duck did not have such prejudices, and nor did she intend to pass them on to her offspring. As a result, they all grew up valuing each other equally and celebrating their differences and whatnot. The duckling never knew that she was 'ugly'. She grew up pretty laid-back, like all the others, and dicked around on the pond a whole lot. Splashing. Quacking. Eating worms, probably.

Then, when she got older, she unexpectedly bloomed into a beautiful swan. Beautiful, that is, in the eyes of folks who care about that sort of thing. Which, of course, her family didn't, and nor did anyone else she loved. In fact, no one noticed.

So, really, there was no story at all.

CINDERELLA

Watching Cinderella put on the slipper, it struck Prince Charming how odd it was that she was the only woman in the kingdom who was a size 8.

There was once a young princess called Ella, whose mother sadly passed away. Her father remarried, then also popped his clogs, leaving Ella the ward of her stepmother.

This stepmother was . . . let's not say 'evil' exactly, such a relative term in Fairyland, with all its blood and cruelty, stealing of firstborns and so forth. But even the queen's BFFs couldn't deny she was on the evil *spectrum*. Unable to stand the sight of Ella, she consigned her to the position of scullery maid and elevated her own two daughters to Ella's former station as crown princesses.

At this time a series of disastrous investment decisions led to a nationwide financial crash, and the royal family found itself suddenly cash poor.

The new queen, no fool, had already pivoted towards digital assets and brand management. She had also swapped a couple of mangy forests for a spanking new-build office block in flashy Silicon Hillock – the only part of the realm impervious to recession.

In these offices, the queen installed Ella's two stepsisters, Olga and Wilhelmina, as the company's CEO and CFO respectively. Sad to say, these two treated the firm as their own private queendom, behaving imperiously towards their wretched employees and earning themselves the conjoined nickname 'the ugly stepsisters'. (The ugliness referred to was spiritual, and not a reference to their looks – with which this story is unconcerned and are not recorded here.)

In a moment of inspiration, the queen put Princess Ella to work as an unpaid intern at the firm. Thus she could inconvenience and humiliate the girl, and save herself some money into the bargain. Ella was expected to work sixteen-hour days cleaning the office, managing the stockroom, and signing for and unloading deliveries.

At the time of this story, the company's biggest product by far was activated charcoal shots (which are for drinking). The shots were going great guns, selling in multiple chains including Wallmoat and Saints Buried. The company had seen solid double-digit four-quadrant growth year-on-year, and were tipped by the clever money as a dominant force (if not a future category killer) in a serious expansion market. At least, so Ella overheard as she changed the photocopy toner.

Traipsing up and down in the service elevator all day as she did, Ella got terribly grimy and dusty. She started to hear others referring to her as 'Cinderella', which she quite liked. It was certainly accurate, after all. Eventually she even began to think of herself as Cinderella.

'Sweetie?' said Olga one afternoon, peering round the door of the delivery bay. 'I'm sorry to ask, but could you put my out-of-office on for me? I've got to rush off for the long weekend.'

'Sure thing,' said Cinderella, appearing from behind a large crate.

'And do Willy's too?' (This was Wilhelmina's nickname.) 'I literally can't even. You *are* a hun. What you up to this weekend? Off somewhere nice?' Olga glanced at her phone, then sniffed the air, not wanting dust on her still-drying nails.

'Uh, no?' said Cinders. 'Big delivery this weekend. I've got to be here.'

'Not coming to the prince's ball?' Olga was scandalized. But excited too. Cinderella was by far the biggest competition for Prince Charming's hand in marriage, and here she was saying she wouldn't be able to attend his birthday ball. Practically every eligible lady on the continent had been invited. Then Olga had a thought that made her heart canter at a happy rate. Was it possible that Cinderella had worked in the bowels of this building so long that people had *forgotten* she was royalty?

'Not unless the prince in question wants to come and help me shift thirty-two pallets to Bay F,' Cinders replied.

'No rest for the wicked.' Olga grimaced sympathetically. 'Still . . .' She sought flailingly for a silver lining. 'Time and a half, I suppose?'

'If I was paid, I guess it might be,' said Cinderella.

Olga couldn't think of a response to this, and nor could she make out her stepsister's expression in the dark. The pause began to stretch, and made them both nervous.

'Best get back,' said Cinders.

'Have a good one,' said Olga. Then, feeling that the remark sounded thoughtless between stepsisters, she added sharply, 'Someone really needs to sort a Doodle poll for that meeting about us going paperless.'

'I'll do it,' said Cinders. 'Easy-peasy.'

'And my printer's broken itself again, yawn. Could you fix?'

'I can make that happen for you,' Cinders replied.

'Totes adorbs,' said Olga, retreating. 'Smiley face crying face kissing face *byeeee*!'

Cinderella sat in the gloom of the delivery bay and breathed a sigh of relief. It was five thirty, and soon enough the office would be entirely empty – and then she could really get to work.

First, though, she went up to her stepsisters' offices on the top floor to put on their out-of-offices. She noticed that a too-thick wad of paper had been petulantly jammed into Olga's printer, so she reset it, then back to the delivery bay.

She turned on the lamp in her little kiosk, and got down to some serious studying for the law degree which no one knew she was taking. At seven, she stretched, yawned, put on the kettle and made herself an instant miso soup. Sipping it, and contemplating a weekend alone in the office, she shivered with satisfaction.

Around ten, too tired to trust herself cycling home in the dark, she went to sleep on her camp bed. And come morning, she was back at her desk. She took charge of the big delivery when it came around lunchtime, then headed out for a walk along the nearby canal to sit in the sun and eat her sandwiches, before getting back to work.

Several hours later, as the early-evening sun finally disappeared from the kiosk window, Cinderella reached out to angle her lamp towards the book she was reading. But it wasn't on. She turned round, wondering where the extra light was coming from. And there, hanging in mid-air and suffused by a bright glow, was a magical-looking woman of late middle age. In her hand she held a wand. She smiled kindly.

Cinders stood up and walked towards her.

'Who the hell are you?' asked Cinderella.

'My dear,' said the apparition. 'I am your Fairy Godmother.'

'Thank balls for that,' said Cinderella. 'I thought I was getting a brain tumour. Or religion.'

'Darling girl,' admonished the other. 'Such language is not ladylike.'

'Quite right,' said Cinderella. 'Cos I ain't no lady.'

This shocked the Fairy Godmother so much her light went out and she fell on her arse with a scream.

'How can you say such a thing?' she said, getting up and rubbing her behind.

'Easily,' said Cinderella. 'What business is it of yours?'

'I'm your *god*mother!'

'So God exists then, does she? I don't remember there being fairies in the Bible. Isn't this all a little . . . culturally muddled?'

'Let's not get bogged down in that right now,' said the FG. 'I want you to be happy. It's my job to make that happen. (God, that hurts.)'

'Here, sit,' said Cinders, pulling over an office chair and brushing off the dust. 'You look knackered.'

'It does take it out of you,' the FG admitted. 'All that

hovering rubbish. But the kiddies like it, you see. I've got to say, it's nice to meet someone normal for a change. Thank you. Ooh!' she squeaked, as Cinders poured her a brandy. 'I really shouldn't. I'm flying home, after all. But medicinally . . .'

The brandy was down the hatch and the glass back in Cinderella's hand in a trice.

'Let me get this straight,' said Cinders, filling the glass a little deeper this time. 'What do I need a fairy godmother for? This is just cheap corner-shop stuff, bee-tee-dubs. Tastes like factory run-off.'

'Does the trick though, durnit?' said FG, tossing back the second measure and handing it to Cinders with a burpo profundo and a giggle. 'If you want to know my opinion, I agree. Godparents are for little ones. But it's not down to me. All *I* know is I have to get to all the addresses on the docket before I can clock off.'

'But I'm a princess,' Cinderella persisted. 'I've got *crazy* privilege. It's coming off me like sweat.'

'And yet here you are, covered in grime, working every hour there is,' said the Fairy Godmother.

'That's because I *like* it that way,' said Cinderella, getting angry. 'Don't you understand? I could stop this tomorrow if I wanted. But it's important to me to understand the meaning of hard work, and experience the value of something earned. I'm trying to escape unfair privilege, and work for a better world. You should go and help some poor girl in a sweatshop with no prospects. Help a bunch of them. A *generation* of them, preferably!'

'People look up to you,' said FG.

'I don't want them to. I want them to enjoy their *own* lives!'

'Well, maybe that's why they look up to you in particular . . .' Seeing the disgust on Cinderella's face, she abandoned that line of argument. 'Listen,' FG said. 'From what I can make out, the forces upstairs are as conservative as those down here. But maybe you can use that to make a difference. Because tonight there's a ball . . . Prince Charming . . .'

'NFI,' said Cinderella.

The Fairy Godmother flourished her hand, there was a distant sound as of icicles jangling together, and she was holding an invitation.

'I'm not going,' said Cinders. 'Some inbred halfwit wandering around his own personal sex buffet? While his Pimpmaster General notes down the women he deems it profitable to impregnate? Not a fun Saturday night, in my book. Presumably there's a swimsuit round?'

'Suit yourself, dearie,' said the FG, getting up and filling her glass from the water cooler. She looked around the loading bay. 'But I'll leave you the fancy get-up required, just in case you have a change of heart.'

She waved her wand in the air while she drank, and a gown appeared draped over the tines of a nearby forklift truck. Matching shoes sparkled into existence on the ground alongside.

'The ball has already started, so I've ordered a special carriage to take you there. It's outside now.' She took the bottle from under Cinderella's arm and held it at arm's length. 'One for the road? Perhaps not,' she said. 'Goes straight to your head after a long day, doesn't it? Hope there's not too much traffic up there or I might be in trouble.'

She pulled a yellow form from deep within the mystery of her blouse and squinted at it. 'Oh, gawd,' she muttered. 'That's a bit of a journey.'

'Help poor people, you idiot!' said Cinderella.

The FG swirled her wand and floated up into the air. 'I'll suggest it to my line manager,' she said.

Then she buggered off.

Cinderella sighed wearily, and turned back to her studies. *People like me*, she thought, *being allotted fairy godmothers. Such total bullshit.* It just made her want to work harder to help the people living in sl–

'Forgot to mention.'

Cinders jumped. The FG was fluttering above her once more.

'If you go to the ball, it's under one condition: you *must* leave by midnight, or everything will go wrong. And it's . . . gone seven now. Shit! Princess Veronika will be in bed.' With a look of deep concentration and a loud popping noise, the FG vanished once more.

Unsure whether the popping noise was a function of magic, or the result of a biological process, Cinders retreated to the nearby bathroom to escape any potential stench. She swept up the gown and shoes as she passed. In the bathroom, she held up the dress in the mirror. And the shoes in front of the dress.

She washed her hands and her face, dried them. Held up the dress again.

It didn't entirely *not* suit her.

She looked in the mirror a while more. And at the shoes. She hadn't been to a ball since when her father was alive. 'Could be fun,' she admitted to her reflection.

When Cinders stepped out of the delivery bay on to the street to order an Ogre, she remembered the smelly old fairy mentioning something about sending a cab. Annoyingly, it was impossible to see if it had turned up, because some antisocial douche had dumped what looked like a three-tonne avocado in the middle of the street.

'*Milady*,' said a voice.

Cinderella jumped. Then she looked up to see an elderly chauffeur sitting on top of the avocado, with reins in his hands. Following the reins, she saw four horses that she had also somehow failed to notice.

A door in the side of the avocado swung open and Cinderella climbed up into it in a daze. It seemed improper not to.

Then, with a slap of the whip, the avocado carriage took off along the street, pushing Cinderella back into the upholstry.

To one side of her seat was a fabulous array of make-up – lipstick, mascara, eyeshadow, blusher – as well as a mirror and a separate chair. The entire arrangement was fixed together on a gimbal to render it immune to the movement of the carriage. (Such sublime thoughtfulness.) Cinderella didn't normally bother with make-up. One more thing women had to worry about that men didn't. After all, Prince Charming probably thought he'd made an effort if someone had combed most of the previous meal's caviar from his twirly moustache. But, looking at her spectacular gown and shoes, she felt *they* deserved a bit of accompaniment, so she got to work.

Just as she thought it was all starting to come together (although, in a perfect world, she'd have had a proper shower rather than a swift, emphatic armpit-scrub with a facecloth), the carriage pulled up.

Cinderella donned the masque that the chauffeur held out to her as he helped her down from the carriage. Never had a tip been so obviously earned, but she hadn't a shilling on her, and begged apology.

'Buy you a Guinness sometime,' she said, giving him a slap on the shoulder. He tilted his head minutely towards her and then melted into the background.

She looked up at the palatial venue, its facade emblazoned (and the air scented) via a thousand multicoloured artisanal candles. She took a deep breath, then started up the wide staircase, suppressing the tremor in her legs with determination.

Past the burly yet polite guards, and in the interior, it was no less of an intimidatingly swanky affair. Gigantic ballroom. Glorious music. Incredible little canapés that Cinderella couldn't help cramming down her neck in case they never came round again. And a glass of fizzy plonk on a silver platter every way you turned.

'Look at all the money spoffed on glad rags in this place, LOL,' she yelled over the music to the first guest who came to talk to her. The woman froze and backed away. *Your loss, love*, thought Cinders.

Clearly, despite wanting desperately to avoid it, Cinders

had made a bit of an impression. Everywhere she turned, groups curled in on themselves and talked, then looked at her. Not in that bitchy, gloating way she knew from the office. This was something else.

Really, Cinderella had only accepted the invitation to have a final glimpse into the world she was fighting against. And also, possibly, to see how badly her sisters fared, because they really had zero sense of style. Although, noticing this thought, she admonished herself for it.

But wait! *There they were.*

Hmm. Not so *awful* . . . and best to steer clear of them, in case they recognized her.

Well, I've seen them now, Cinderella thought. *Had my fun. Maybe just one more canapé – yum. And just one more glass. Then out* . . .

Happening to glance over at her stepsisters again, she noticed something odd. Both of them were staring wide-eyed, their looks travelling across the dancefloor with a steady, unwavering movement, right . . . towards . . . her?

'Do you mind if I ask you to dance?'

'Ulp.' Cinders coughed some champagne through her nose. Her eyes watered as she tried to swallow both the champagne and the mouthful of canapé at once. She was not usually so discomfited by the attentions of a man, but her mind had been elsewhere.

'Sure, whatever,' she said. 'But be warned, I stink.'

He did not acknowledge this as an obstacle. Taking her hands, he instantly swept her away with the music in a one-two-three-one-two-three that was (she admitted) rather splendid.

'You don't like to dance?' There was a pleasing bass vibration to his voice.

'Never tried,' she said. 'Always thought it was a waste of time.'

'What do you do instead?'

'Eat babies,' she said. 'Rob old people. Just the really weak ones.'

'Is it fun?'

'It passes the time. Watch your feet, Goddammit.'

'Actually, my feet were supposed to be there. What do you think of dancing now?'

He was an exquisite dancer. And, after the first introductory stumble, he had succeeded in making Cinders feel as though she were too. He guided her with a delicate assurance that made her feel as though she were doing it herself. The lights spun somewhat. The champagne softened everything. Or sharpened it.

'Jury's out,' she said, realizing that her mouth was somehow next to his ear. From his skin she caught the trace of cologne. It was entirely exotic to her. Well, it would have to be, in comparison with eau de photocopy toner.

'It's fun, I suppose,' she said, 'but also pointless.'

'I don't see how spending time with you could ever be pointless.'

In the rhythmic swirl of music and dance, Cinders found it irritatingly hard to keep hold of her next rebuke. So she remained silent for a few moments during which their movements and the music made it hard to think of anything at all.

'You've no idea who I am,' she said at last. 'I could

actually eat babies, for all you know. Dancing together for five minutes is not a sensible basis on which to build a relationship.'

'We've been dancing for half an hour,' he said.

At this moment in the dance, it was necessary for him to throw her back and lean over her. The posture had certain connotations, and at that moment she happened to lose her breath. When he filled her view like this, the lights in the room failed to reveal him as a phony or a grotesque. In fact, the features she'd thought handsome from afar were even better in close-up. The prince leaned closer, and the room was suddenly deathly quiet.

She could have kicked him in the knackers, but as a royal doing so might start a war between their respective countries. The War of the Prince's Bollocks did have a certain ring, but she decided against it.

Her second option was to kiss him and enjoy it for what it was, seeing as he *was* a bit of a knockout. But he'd practically take that as engagement. And in front of all these posh freaks? No.

Her third option was this: to say, 'Hey, just cos I swish into the room and happen to have scrubbed up, don't take that as part of *your* narrative. I might well be the perfect woman (I do my best) but I'm not the perfect woman *for you*. Even if I was interested, amazing as this must be to you, I've got my own life going on. I'm not even mildly tempted to throw it all away to be your favourite toy for a couple of weeks or months. Folks like you don't see women as complex beings; just apparitions who *complete* or *fix* you. So, laters.'

But this wasn't the time or the place for a big speech. Besides, he'd probably take it as her just wanting him to try harder. No. There was a much simpler and more eloquent way of saying the same thing.

Prince Charming (for of course that's who he was – a fact confirmed by the way the congregation had retreated to the edges of the room to watch the two of them dance) froze as Cinderella deftly wriggled out of his grip, and walked away from him across the ballroom.

Oh, ballbags, Cinders thought. *I've done it now.*

Attempting to appear casual as she weaved through the crowd towards the door, she glanced at a clock and saw it was one minute before midnight.

'Out of my way, posh dickheads!' she called. 'Coming through!'

Once out of the door, she took her high heels off and sprinted in bare feet. However, as she came out at the top of the outside staircase, she skidded gracelessly on the carpet and toppled over. As she clattered to the ground, she thought she caught a glimpse of the prince between people's legs, staring woefully in her direction.

But there was no time. She leaped back on her pins, careened down to the street and hurdled through the proffered door of the magic avocado (there's a sentence you don't write every day etc. etc.). She lay on the floor panting until she was convinced they were out of sight. She noticed she seemed to have dropped one shoe. But that was her smallest concern right now.

She clambered up, still out of breath, and plumped herself among the cushions, grateful to have escaped. She was just starting to take an interest in the contents of the onboard minibar when –

WHUMF!

The carriage exploded.

Only joking. It turned back into an avocado. And Cinderella's clothes returned to rags (or at least, very dirty and ripped jeans), and the make-up she had been wearing vanished, along with the horses and driver. She found herself sitting on the road next to a ripe avocado.

A walk and some fresh air would do her good. Plus an avocado for sustenance! 'Booyah!' she said. And then wondered if people still said that.

The following Monday, the office was alive with gossip about Prince Charming, who was certainly among the most exciting princes in all the realms. (There were a few handsomer ones, it's true, but they tended to be very interested in murder. Or penises.)

It seemed the prince was obsessed with someone he had met at his birthday ball the previous Saturday. It was such a talking point that some people in the office even mentioned it to Cinderella, someone they never usually spoke to at all.

'Crazy,' she said. 'I wonder who it was?'

'Apparently, she just vanished. And *no one knows who she was!*'

'Woah. That's wild. Well, she's certainly not me, that's for sure!' said Cinderella. She cursed herself for being such a terrible improviser when nervous, but it turned out OK because nobody noticed or listened to her. Even if she had shouted it from the rooftops (or even worse, sent an all-staff company email), admitting that she was the mystery girl, no one would have believed her. In fact, that would probably have convinced people she was definitely *not* telling the truth.

And so Cinderella returned peacefully to her work. The latest round of lay-offs meant her job now included delivering the post, and she heard much delightful badinage as she pushed her mail trolley through the offices. Discussions of the latest hangings, sports results, invasions and so forth.

She went on with her life, and focused on revising her law books whenever she could.

Then, one day, Cinderella saw some colleagues laughing over a newspaper and, as she went past, she leaned in for a look. It was the 'Brief Encounters' column.

'*We met at the ball,*' it said. '*We danced, you fled. Marriage?*' She fled.

Then, one weekend a few months later, when Cinderella was becoming dull-witted with the routine of office life and had several loads of dirty washing to do, she returned to the palace.

Usually, Cinders stayed below the stairs, where the conversation was lively, people were friendly, and you didn't have to spend meals with a stepmother who wanted to kill you.

Nipping up the back stairs just to have a look at her old bedroom, she heard a familiar voice. That satisfying bass, that confident tone. At the sound she got a sense memory of a certain cologne.

Retreating down the stairs and along a corridor, Ella moved close to the entrance of the morning room, and peered round the door. Inside, she saw her ghastly stepsisters smiling and mincing about in the most pretentious way. Kneeling before them was Prince Charming. Each princess stepped forward in turn and tried to shove, squeeze and finally ram her foot into the shoe he was holding. The prince was, in fact, being quite charming by pretending that he thought either stepsister might have been the woman he had danced with.

When their exertions proved fruitless, and a certain amount of blood was seeping from each misapplied ankle, the prince said, 'It's extraordinary. A soothsayer told me that the girl who matched this shoe grew up in this house. Your Highnesses, I earnestly entreat your pardon for intruding upon your day. My search must move elsewhere . . .'

Cinders stole silently back to the safety of the servants' quarters, leaving the prince discreetly dabbing the sisters' gore from the shoe with his kerchief, before placing it in his pocket.

The next thing that people were talking about in the office was the online campaign to find Prince Charming's mysterious girl.

'What's an online campaign?' asked Cinderella when she heard. But everyone knew that everyone knew that. So no one told her.

She soon worked it out though. Apparently, posters showing the specific footprint of the shoe worn by the mystery girl had been left on washing lines all over the kingdom, boasting a handsome reward (handsomeness in everything being very on-brand for Prince C) in case anyone could find a footprint that matched it.

'Maybe she doesn't want to be found,' she said.

Cinders felt she'd made a few decent quips in the office over the years – not that anyone had ever noticed. This remark, however, intended in perfect seriousness, caused general hilarity. It was unthinkable that anyone could not want to marry into royalty and enormous wealth. Everybody fell about. Someone even hi-fived her. She pushed her trolley dejectedly away.

For the thousandth time, Cinderella battled to get the trolley's wonky front wheel over the lip of the service elevator. When the lift opened on the bottom floor, she yanked the recalcitrant vehicle out after her and angled it in the right direction with a great deal of sweaty effort and furious swearing. Finally she got it back in its place and turned around, exhausted.

'Oh, shit,' she said.

'Yes,' said Prince Charming.

'You shouldn't be here,' she said. 'It's employees only. More importantly, it's stalking.'

'What can I say?' he replied. 'I don't know how to give up.'

'It's probably a brain defect,' she said, 'caused by your inbreeding.' And then she reminded herself: *Don't try to run him down. It won't work. He's literally Prince Charming.*

He smiled at her.

'How did you find me?' she asked.

'It turns out you are so ridiculously assiduous that you dust the cobwebs from the office ceiling, princess.'

'Don't call me that,' she said. 'I really don't like it. So what?'

'You were standing on the photocopier dusting, and when you leaned over you must have pressed the button with a toe, and left a photocopy of your foot.'

'So someone found it, and matched it to the picture, and told you?'

He smiled.

'What was the reward for dobbing me in?' she asked. 'I bet it was thousands. I should have claimed it myself and given it to charity.'

'Does this shoe fit you?' he asked, getting down on one knee and holding it out.

'Of course it does; it's my shoe.'

'Won't you try it on?'

'No.'

He smiled again.

'Would you mind going now?' she asked.

He raised an eyebrow. 'Won't you come with me?'

'No! I've got work to do. Thanks.'

'If you come with me,' he said, 'you'll never have to work again.'

'I never had to work in the first place,' she said, looking at her dusty hands and wiping them on her backside, 'if I didn't want to. You know that. So throw out the damsel-rescuing routine, OK? It's out of date and it stinks.'

He was crestfallen. More than that – he looked genuinely stung. Even though she knew this was because he was spoiled, it made her feel guilty.

'Look,' she said. 'Getting sent here was an incredible opportunity. I've always *hated* being royalty. Not allowed to help the poor and starving, or even *talk* to them. Because it wasn't *the done thing*. When my stepmother put me in this job, I saw it was a lifeline – an extremely useful life experience that a normal princess never normally gets. I welcomed it.'

'Great,' said Prince Charming, rallying. 'But I'd say after all this time you've got that experience, right? And you can take your rightful place as a princess – and a future queen – better prepared to rule than any of her predecessors.'

'Hey, I'm sorry,' said Cinderella. She even patted him on the knee. 'I know no one has ever said this to you before. I am not interested. I know you found it exciting to chase your magical pretend woman through a long campaign. It made you feel like the hero in a story. And everyone you know is invested in it too, because everything always works out for you and therefore you think it will end in marriage and children. But it won't.'

The prince had now adopted a patient, thoughtful expression, and still affected a slightly humorous air. He put up his hands. 'I'm sorry that I came on a bit strong.'

'The national campaign thing *is* on the strong side, that's true,' Cinderella said. 'But, really, the thing is I'm *just, not, interested*. Whichever way you ask me.'

This time she watched it sink in with a little guilty satisfaction.

'I'm *eighteen*,' she said. 'Who gets married at eighteen? I'm studying towards a law degree, so I can help people in the slums who have no rights. After studying, I'm going travelling. To have some real experiences. And fend for myself, like real people do.'

It had obviously never occurred to Prince Charming that a person (still less a beautiful privileged woman) could want these things when there was an easy alternative.

'After travelling, I'm going to have a career. Find a place in my chosen industry. And, let's face it, probably shag around a bit. Then maybe settle into a solid relationship. If I meet someone.'

Prince Charming appeared to be making some rapid calculations. 'If I wait all that time . . .' he said with strangulated seriousness.

'Don't be stupid, Prince,' she said. 'Hey, what is your name, anyway? I can't call you Prince all the time.'

'Hector Bartolomeo Randolph Charmant-Schleswig-Branden-Försstenweis von Engelscharpff.'

'Right, right. Well. Prince it is.'

'I wasn't finished –'

'Let's do the rest some other time,' she snapped. 'Who wants to be in a royal family anyway? The scrutiny, the psychological problems, the isolation, the responsibility, the pressure.'

The prince started to look like he was waking up from an alarming dream. He glanced at his brocaded sleeves and at the inherited medals on his breast. 'What am I wearing?' he said. 'This should be worn by a retired soldier.'

Cinderella was pleased to witness his awakening. But she really *did* have some invoices to go through, so she popped a pencil in her mouth and flicked over some pages on her clipboard.

'I should be wearing ripped working man's trousers!' the prince exclaimed.

'Mm-hmm. They're called jeans.'

'And going to music festivals! And smoking jazz cigarillos! God, I can't believe I have lived like this for so long. It's so *false*.'

'Say it, bro,' murmured Cinderella, adding up some figures in her head.

'From now on, I want to live a *real* life, giving back to people instead of leeching off them! I'll revoke my royal status and become a doctor. I'll work in the world's most dangerous war zones! Bringing relief to the oppressed!'

'That's the stuff.' She flicked over a page and popped the pencil back behind her ear.

'I want to begin now!' he yelled with joy.

'Well, if you want to start understanding the working man right away, there's some boxes here that need to be taken up to the fifth floor,' Cinderella said.

And so Prince Charming gave up his titles and lands, and devoted his life to good causes. Cinders and he became friends and colleagues, and soon afterwards fellow students. On a couple of occasions they got drunk and emotional, and lay fully clothed next to each other pretending to be asleep. Then, gradually, as time passed and their lives became busier, they lost touch and forgot about each other. Then they died. That's life, innit.

THREE LITTLE PIGS

'OK, I'm potentially on board with a house made of straw
but what's the broadband like?'

The wolf anxiously pushed open the door to the estate agents' office. Inside, the air was stuffy. His fur was uncomfortably matted beneath this collar that he wasn't used to wearing. He felt out of sorts. But he straightened the folder under his arm and walked over to the front desk.

'I have an appointment,' he said.

'Excuse me,' said the rosy-cheeked pig receptionist, flashing a bright smile at him for a fraction of a second before speaking into her headset. 'Pigtons Estate Agents, may I put you on hold? Thank you. Yes, sir?'

It took the wolf a moment to realize the receptionist was talking to him, and then he worried that he'd lost his chance, because she said the same sentence again to another caller. He noticed that she gave the same intensely bright smile to the callers, even though they couldn't see it.

'Yes, sir?' she said.

'I've got an appointment with Mr Pigton!' he blurted as fast as he could.

'Of course. I'll tell him you're here. Please take a seat.'

The wolf sat on the edge of a seat next to a giant water cooler. He was very thirsty, but he was also nervous and felt he'd drop the water or make a mess or something. God, he hated being nervous. His *eyes* hurt. He was sure he was blinking too much. Should he have trimmed his claws?

'Mr Wolf!' said a jolly voice, and a large, youngish pig wearing a bright tie appeared from the office beyond. They shook hands, which Mr Wolf always found awkward. He knew he oughtn't, but he found pig trotters awfully moist and clammy. And he knew that his paw must be very dry and furry to the other.

'Come with me!' said the beaming estate agent. 'The car's outside. I've got a few places I think you'll just love.'

As they pulled on to the road, Mr Wolf shrank down in his seat, ashamed to be seen in a branded Pigtons car.

Mr Pig was oblivious to his discomfort and chatted away merrily all through the journey. 'It's just on the market,' he was saying. 'Really nice place. You married? Got kids?'

'No,' said Mr Wolf. 'It's just me. I've worked really hard to get to this point. Actually,' he admitted, surprising himself, 'this all makes me kind of nervous.'

'Ha!' said Mr Pig as he parked up. 'Don't worry. I'm here to make your dreams come true.' He jumped out and stood there jingling the keys in his hand while Mr Wolf tried to angle himself out of the tiny car without doing something lastingly unpleasant to his neck.

Mr Wolf's heart had been sinking from the start of the journey, when Mr Pig had turned left out of the office car park and headed towards the slums. There was an unspoken judgement in it that dragged at Mr Wolf's soul.

'Good location, behind a popular restaurant,' said Mr Pig, ducking his head out of the way of a cloud that came laden with the smell of hot oil. The 'restaurant' was a nasty little hovel serving fried pigeon in paper bags to what his mother would have called the 'wrong sort' of wolves, who threw their food on the pavement outside the restaurant, then pounced and devoured it there, leaving the bones for the rats.

They made their way down the side of the building, ignoring the refuse underfoot, and Mr Pig opened the front door. 'Here's the bedroom,' he said.

'Where's the kitchen?' asked Mr Wolf. Mr Pig pointed to an alcove at the back of the room.

'I can't see anything,' complained Mr Wolf. He knew already that he could never live here. But for god's sake, at least he should be allowed a look at the place. He pulled back a curtain and light flooded in to reveal a strange form wriggling under a blanket on the floor.

Mr Pig and Mr Wolf both jumped back in terror.

The blanket was yanked back by an elderly, bloated wolf. Bunches of the fur on his head were gone, from burn and bite scars.

'What the bloody hell are you doing here?' he yelled. A young vixen squirmed out of sight beneath the blanket next to him.

'The landlord said it would be OK to have a look at the place,' said Mr Pig. Mr Wolf looked up at the walls, which, where they weren't terribly stained, were covered with religious memorabilia and posters of famous wolf musicians from yesteryear.

Mr Wolf retreated while Mr Pig stayed behind making his apologies, or explanations, or whatever. He sat in the car looking at his knees.

'Well!' said Mr Pig brightly, starting the car. 'You can see how much scope there is for improvement. With a little investment, you could make it a really great place – make it your *own* – and of course that's reflected in the price.'

Mr Wolf nodded, looking out of the car window, as Mr Pig talked on about how the place was begging for a first-time buyer to fix it up and double its value. Down an alleyway, he saw a dog's corpse covered in flies lying among some litter. Then just as he opened his mouth to point it out, the dog took a ragged breath and the flies rose into the air, before settling again.

'It's a really vibrant wolf neighbourhood,' said Mr Pig. 'Lots of great restaurants. Terrific atmosphere. Music.'

'It's made of straw,' said Mr Wolf with a sigh.

'Yeah, of course. I mean, they all are. Aren't they?' said Mr Pig, checking his mirror as he moved out on to the main road. 'Round here, I mean.'

It was a few months later that Mr Wolf next entered the offices of Pigtons. He was feeling no less nervous, but this time he had a steely determination not to show it.

'Appointment with Mr Pig,' he said, before the receptionist could play any of her tricks. 'I'll wait.'

The wait was shorter this time. And, when she appeared, Ms Pig (Mr Wolf understood it was a firm of three siblings) was slightly older, slightly plumper and more smartly dressed.

'I brought my car,' said Mr Wolf, once they had shaken hands.

Ms Pig turned out to be just as chatty as her brother. Mr Wolf preferred driving while they spoke, it meant he wasn't at a loss with nothing to do.

'You're young to be a homeowner,' said Ms Pig.

'You mean for a wolf?' Mr Wolf said.

'Certainly not. It's almost impossible for young people to get a mortgage these days. And, even when they can, they can't afford the places they want. I suppose you're like everyone else, and you've had a bit of help from the Bank of Mum and Dad?'

Mr Wolf turned to look at the pig to see if she was for real.

'I mean, have they remortgaged to give you an early inheritance?'

Mr Wolf wanted to tell Ms Pig that she didn't seem to know very much about how wolf families worked. And to mind her own business. Instead, he satisfied himself with: 'Let's just concentrate on the property, shall we?'

'Of course!' said Ms Pig. 'Sorry – I'm just talking nonsense. Such a chatterpig. Here's the place. On the left. As you can see, it's a nice neighbourhood.'

Mr Wolf could see. It was delightfully suburban. Children were playing. There was a gardener trimming the strip of green on the opposite side of the street (a wonderfully contented summer sound) and a postman with his bag over his shoulder.

'People moan about piggification,' Ms Pig said, following Mr Wolf's gaze, 'but I don't see the problem. Seems to me it just means making things nicer. You *can* afford the mortgage, you say?' She smiled brightly at Mr Wolf as they crossed the lawn.

'Yes,' said Mr Wolf. 'I used to have my own business helping wolves from deprived backgrounds with their own tech start-ups. I sold it to Gargoyle. Now I'm mostly on the Shed Talk circuit.'

Ms Pig whistled. He *could* afford the mortgage then. She held the door for Mr Wolf. Inside was a dim dankness and a smell that tickled Mr Wolf's nostrils awfully.

'Did someone die here?' he asked.

'I couldn't tell you,' said Ms Pig. 'I mean, I have hundreds of properties on my books. It's possible. I'm not going to say it's *impossible*. Don't you think that most houses have had someone die in them? Statistically? There's a lovely little fishpond in the garden. Quiet neighbours. And look at the walls. Twigs. You like that, right?'

Mr Wolf had seen enough. He'd *smelled* enough just stepping in the front door. But the decision not to bother removing all the CRIME SCENE: ENTER YE NOT tape from the doorways, nor to clean or mask the bloodstains on the walls, clearly showed the esteem that prospective buyers were held in.

Mr Wolf got back in his own car and sat there fuming. He chose not to notice the fact that everyone on the street – the kids playing, the gardener mowing and the postman in his shorts – had stopped and stared the second they'd spotted him. They were all pigs.

Ms Pig got into the car next to him.

'Shall we see some more?' Ms Pig asked.

'Not if they're made of twigs,' Mr Wolf said. 'I told you quite clearly on the phone what I was looking for. And twigs was not it. I was very clear straw was unacceptable. Twigs might as well be straw, as far as I'm concerned. I'm a busy wolf and I don't like being messed around like this.'

Ms Pig flipped open her folder of other potential houses. 'I sold a twig house on this street last week for three quarters of a million,' she said.

It was a number of months later. Mr Wolf entered the offices of Pigtons wearing dark glasses, and went to sit straight on one of the chairs. The grinning receptionist knew him by now, and alerted Mr Pig.

This time there was nothing like the wait of the two previous occasions. The third Pig sibling came straight through from the office beyond. He had a fat folder under his arm. He wore rimless spectacles. He was the eldest of the three, and the most corpulent. But he wore it better. His suit was a good fit, a pleasingly expensive soft, dark fabric with wickedly narrow pinstripes, and he had a sober frankness that was a welcome change from the aggravating falsity of his younger siblings.

'I got us a cab,' he said over his spectacles. 'Save us driving. Also, Pippa here will get us a coffee, if you'd like. I'm having a macchiato.'

Mr Wolf was not used to people fetching him coffees without him asking. He accepted on principle, just so he'd be able to recall what it was like should it never happen again.

'I'll have the same,' he said.

'The car's here,' said Mr Pig, looking at his phone. He led the way out, then stood squinting into the sun as he held the car door for Mr Wolf. He was slightly sweaty and out of breath, and once they were in the car together he got to business at once.

'I'm horrified about how my brother and sister treated your business here with us,' he said, the moment the cab vroomed away from the lot. 'Quite frankly, I'm amazed you've come to give us a third chance. And I'm certainly not going to waste it.' He gave a big smile, which most unexpectedly transformed his features into something likeable.

'I'm glad to hear it,' said Mr Wolf, taking a sip of his macchiato. He took off his dark glasses and tucked them in his top pocket. 'Your siblings didn't seem to believe that I was a regular customer. They thought I must have inherited my money. Or perhaps stolen it.'

Mr Pig shook his head impatiently. 'They haven't been doing this as long as I have, Mr Wolf,' he said. 'They suffer from prejudices that they ought to be able to see past. Not that I'm making excuses. I'm not. I'm very happy to have your business. I know your money is completely legitimate. And I want you to enjoy the fruits of it.'

Before Mr Wolf could reply, the car came to a halt.

They both got out, and Mr Pig looked at him. 'What do you think?'

Mr Wolf had to swallow twice before he could answer. 'It's wonderful. Just wonderful. I could afford this?'

Mr Pig nodded. 'Not just afford it. You could *buy* it. When I saw how you'd been messed around, and what sort of a customer you really were, I had the mortgage pre-approved. Up here on the hill, with this view –' he took a deep breath of fresh air – 'it's not quite a gated community, but it ain't far off. You've got the money, you've got the place.'

'Mr Pig!' shouted Mr Wolf. 'You've got yourself a deal! Where do I put my name?'

Mr Pig smiled cordially as he flicked through his porkfolio, offering Mr Wolf several pages to sign.

'I'll need your passport too,' he said. 'I'll get it copied and brought back to you.'

Mr Wolf handed it over.

'And your birth certificate,' said Mr Pig. 'Did I mention that?'

'You did,' said Mr Wolf. 'Not sure why, but whatever. If it makes the process quicker, here it is.'

'Bada bing! All nice and done, and done nice, as my father would say,' said Mr Pig, with a slightly new note entering his accent. 'You stay here and have a look around, let me go downtown and get this paperwork sorted. I'll be back in an hour with everything in place.'

'Mr Pig,' said Mr Wolf, 'how can I possibly thank you?'

'And what did you say back to that?' asked the youngest Pig.

'What do you think?' said the eldest Pig, topping up his brother's bowl with another ladleful of stew.

'Ooh, I just love the ending,' said Ms Pig, her cheeks shining with glee. 'Tell us again! Please!' She slurped her stew greedily.

'OK,' said the oldest brother. 'Well. When that damn wolf finally got to see a house that he liked – one that was made of bricks . . .'

The other two gurgled with laughter.

'No, seriously,' said their big brother. 'Seriously, now. A wolf *could* own a house of bricks . . .'

They all cracked up then, and were helpless for a few minutes, mopping their eyes, and clapping each other on the back. The idea of it! When the hilarity died down, they each had another sip of white wine and a few more mouthfuls of stew, before the eldest brother went on.

'But I could see he was a classic case. So grateful. And I told him –'

'This is my favourite bit,' said Ms Pig.

'I told him that the only thing a new owner has to do is climb up to the top of the chimney and attach the TV aerial, since we can't do it ourselves as it's not covered in our insurance.'

'And he did it?' said the youngest, excited.

'He couldn't wait. I watched him clamber all the way up there,' said Mr Pig. 'Claw against brick, claw against brick. Click, clack, panting, sweating. And smiling all the while. Then, when he had reached the top and was standing on the chimney, all precarious, I asked him who the hell he thought he was to come and live in an area like this. I *shouted* it.'

'And he slipped?' whispered Ms Pig.

'Well, all the grease I put round the edge of the chimney did most of the work,' said Mr Pig, grinning. 'And down he fell, right into the pot.'

'Damn good he tastes too,' said the youngest sibling, taking another mouthful.

A while later, when the stew was all eaten up, and the bowls and pot washed and put away, the three rosy-cheeked estate agents left the house of bricks. They locked the front door behind them, and got into their car and drove home. They left the 'FOR SALE' sign where it was, at the edge of the lawn. Where passers-by could see it, and read the logo:

PIGTONS ESTATE AGENTS: A WARM HEARTH.

SLEEPING BEAUTY

*Everyone in the crowd was terribly embarrassed
that she hadn't simply picked something from
the gift list at Johnne Lewis's Shoppe.*

Once upon a time in Fairyland, there was a princess who was an only child, born late. This meant, of course, that her parents were a total nightmare and worried themselves sick over everything. Nothing was too much for their special girl; she was, after all, their little princess. They dressed her in pink dresses, curled her hair in blonde ringlets and gave her princess-appropriate toys to play with.

They constantly worried that she was coming down with something (which she often was, because children do), and they kept on retainer a troupe of weary medics who offered the same old remedies, whether they worked or not (which they didn't, really).

The doctors would patiently insist that the princess didn't have whatever rare ailment the parents imagined, but instead simply had an earache, or a tummy ache, or the flu, or chicken pox.

(At the chicken-pox diagnosis the realm endured a poultry-free diet for a full calendar year after the queen reflexively ordered all chickens be slaughtered and disposed of in the safest and fastest way then known: deep-fried and fed to people going home from pubs. It went down in history as the Year of KFC, or 'kill the effing chickens'.)

The royals had their daughter homeschooled, and she was educated in the history of princesses, the correct way to use cutlery and how to get out of a carriage without showing your knickers. She was never taught about anything that didn't relate to royalty, as they didn't want to upset her with concepts like death and poor people.

So, as you might imagine, the princess grew up believing the world consisted of people exactly like her. She thought the servants had palaces of their own (albeit smaller ones), and she felt in her heart that anyone could be a princess if they just tried hard enough.

When the princess's sixteenth birthday came along, the king and queen could not resist holding a giant festival in celebration of their wonderful daughter. People brought gifts from far and wide, and pageants were held in her honour.

But everything came to a crashing halt on the morning of the grand feast, when the princess was discovered unconscious on her bedroom floor.

The castle was thrown into a state of panic and despair. The finest doctors in the land were called for. Of course, they were already there, just at the end of the corridor.

'She's in a coma,' they agreed.

'Caused by what?' the queen asked.

'It could be any one of a number of –'

'It's an allergic reaction!' the queen screamed.

The message radiated outwards through the gathered crowd. Up and down, great multitudes groaned and gnashed their teeth.

The experts stood at the princess's bedside – around four dozen of them – watching her slumber.

'What could she be allergic to?' asked the queen.

'It could be fur,' said one courtier.

'Fur!' said the queen. 'I'm allergic to it myself. It must be that!'

At once, all fur items throughout the castle were destroyed. (All of them, that is, except for the king's ermine coronation get-up. It had belonged to his great-great-grandfather Frederick XVI. Or was that his great-great-*great*-grandfather? It was bloody historical, either way, so he only pretended to burn it, and in fact had it buried in an ivory chest behind the real tennis court.)

After every scrap of fur in the castle had been destroyed, and the entire place thoroughly aired to eradicate any final trace, a duke who was a blood relation to the princess remembered that his aunt had a nut allergy.

'What kind of nut?' asked the king.

'Every kind?' he said. 'I think?'

The crowd descended to the kitchen en masse, and purged it of nuts.

'And legumes!' said a voice. 'While we're here!'

No one was sure who had said it, but the voice carried authority, and so, 'Burn the legumes!' went the cry.

The well-meaning crowd returned from their exertions to the princess's bedside rather giddy and tired, and with their hair flecked with ash. Yet before them the princess slept on, her face tranquil and exquisite.

'It could be the detergent used on her sheets. I had terrible trouble with my skin before I switched detergents,' said a countess. '*And* conditioner.'

The detergent-manufacturer royal and the conditioner-procurer general (albeit these were largely ceremonial posts) were both cast out on their ears in favour of newer, younger blood.

Other members of the royal household shared anecdotes about allergies to shellfish and dairy. It was but an hour's work to close down the three sellers of shellfish in this part of Fairyland, which was a landlocked kingdom. To be honest, no one could work out how they'd lasted so long anyway.

Ridding the land of dairy, however, was a lengthy, painful process. Dairy farmers had to be compensated (like their poultry-farming brethren before them) for their losses, the culling of the nation's herd had to be overseen and then dairy alternatives introduced to the market, such as margarine, rapeseed oil and a plethora of alternative milks. (But not almond or cashew, obviously. Nuts.)

More theories followed. One by one, the nation stripped from its life all things that anyone had ever heard of someone being allergic to. Pineapples, bamboo, wool, feathers, mites, cobwebs, pollen, dust, grass, soap, lead, guns, unicorns and face paint.

Nothing worked.

The princess slept on.

*

There eventually came a point at which life had to reassert its old rhythms and continue without the princess. This happened, but only outside the castle.

Within, life remained on hiatus. Members of her family couldn't bring themselves to leave her bedside, sure there must be something they could do to wake her, if they could only riddle out what it was.

A witch on her way down from her chamber at the top of the castle (where she lived with six cats, and survived on a diet of nuts, legumes, shellfish and dairy – although that's by the by) alighted at the princess's bedroom door and beheld the sad assembly.

This was the witch who had, in fact, been demonized at the princess's baptism for warning that exactly this might happen. She had only had the child's best interests at heart, and yet she had been branded as an evil . . . well, witch. And banished to her tower. (From which she couldn't be removed thanks to a tremendously sturdy clause in her original tenancy agreement, which had been signed, in triplicate, in blood of newt.)

In truth, the witch was a good-hearted soul and she knew her stuff when it came to medicine. At the infant's christening, she had simply been trying to warn the parents (knowing, as she did, the child's restricted gene pool) not *on any account* to fail to have the child vaccinated. But the second she'd brought needles into the thing, everyone had got hysterical, so the witch had withdrawn, tutting and sighing, to her tower.

Meanwhile, the king and queen, quite uneducated themselves and prey to any woo-woo snake-oil practitioner who wandered in off the street, had their minds twisted by old spouses' tales about vaccines. How they made you turn into a raven if administered on a Thursday. How they were only created to further the sale of badger saliva (a chief ingredient, admittedly, and which *had* gone up in value since their inception). So the king and queen failed to heed the witch's warning, and did not get the princess vaccinated.

And, now, here was the unfortunate result: the princess had fallen victim to a sleeping sickness that hadn't been seen in these parts for three hundred years.

'Not since I was in my eighties,' the witch recalled wistfully.

Although these idiots had brought it upon themselves, the witch still felt sorry for them. Chances were, the girl would pull through at some point – but, for the time being, she remained trapped in a coma while her depleted immune system fought a battle that could go either way.

The witch cast a spell on the assembly, putting them into a perpetual trance while their beloved princess still slumbered. Then she trotted back up the 290 steps to her chambers, before remembering she'd actually popped out for cat food. Whereupon she swore vilely, and leaned against a bookshelf waiting for her breath to return.

The castle was trapped in silence. While life continued outside, ivy and thorns grew over the previously pristine walls. Soon, the walls were covered and the castle was lost in a giant thicket. For a hundred years, the castle itself became forgotten.

Then, one day, a true-hearted and noble prince read about the castle and rode there on his horse.

After dismounting and fighting his way through the thorns, he found himself in front of the sleeping beauty. His heart was lost at once. He knew he must wake her. And, if he knew his fairy tales (although they were just called 'tales' where he came from), then true love's kiss would do the trick. Except that no gentleman would dream of kissing a sleeping girl in this day and age.

He thought for a while, before hitting on a solution.

The prince rode back into town and found a jeweller, who he asked to fashion a beautiful necklace with a pendant on it in the shape of a flower. A flower which might also be said to look like a pair of lips. He paid the jeweller handsomely, then gave one side of the pendant a loving kiss. He rode back to the sleeping beauty's side and pressed her lips against the reverse of the pendant – in effect, them kissing.

She awoke and sat up, looking around her.

'Hey,' she said.

'Hey,' he agreed bashfully.

She took in the fact that he was a total hottie along with a blur of other realizations. Why was she in her jimmy-jams? And what was her entire extended family and the whole palace staff doing snoozing around her bed? She rubbed her temples and blinked several times.

'I hope you don't mind me waking you up like this,' the prince said. 'I think you've been in some sort of coma.'

'EXCUSE ME! Can you all get out of my bedroom, please?' she said to the thousand sleepers on the floor around her bed, who began to stir. Then she turned back to the prince. 'Did you just kiss me while I was asleep?'

There was something in her eyes that hadn't been there before. She was suddenly seeing everything anew.

'Why are all the women in this room wearing dresses?'

The multitude of royals, gentry and servants were woozily coming to. Their beloved princess was awake. She was alive!

'That's what women wear, Your Highness,' a maid said.

'But do you all like them? Honestly?'

Compelled to honesty, many of the women shook their heads.

'May it please your ladyship,' said one servant. 'I feel much comfier in chinos.'

'Let women wear chinos, then,' she said. 'And men dresses if they feel like it. Plus – am I mad – but why is *everyone* in this room white? Have all the non-white people died?'

This was a much more uncomfortable question. Her subjects confessed that, no, this was not the case.

'So what do non-white people do? When it comes to representation in the palace, and in the halls of power?'

Silence greeted her.

'Huh,' she said. 'I see. And why are you all standing around my bed? Is that normal? I think there should be a few changes around here. And, while I'm about it, what the effing aitch is going on with those tapestries?'

Everyone turned, blinking, to see what she meant. No

one had looked at the tapestries for centuries. They were just what covered the walls.

'Do my eyes deceive me or are all the women naked and all the men in suits of armour?'

There was a murmur of agreement.

'Well,' she said. 'Let's get some women tapestry weavers in here with some new plans. Maybe have some with lots of women in gorgeous costumes and a bunch of pretty blokes with their dongs out. Even up the score. What do you think?'

Her eye settled again on the prince who had woken her up. He smiled. 'Sounds good to me, milady.'

'I ain't yours nor anyone else's, so check your privilege.'

He bowed. 'I was only using an outdated form of speech. Nevertheless, may I chaperone you to the Ritzy Kino in East Fairyland this evening? They do these great pulled-pork sliders, with loaded chilli-cheese fries, and the new Greta Gerwig film's on. About a free-spirited young wo–'

'I don't know what any of those things are, but sure,' the princess said. 'But first, sod off for an hour. I've got to go and do one of the world's longest toilets. And then I need to work out how I feel about shaving my legs.'

The prince bowed and withdrew.

And everywhere around him, he saw a castle getting to grips with ideas long overdue. In this was a new form of beauty. No longer sleeping, but miraculously woke.

THE
FROG
PRINCE

'I'm not looking for a quick hook-up, you know? I want
someone I can see myself spawning with.'

The frog lurked self-consciously on the corner. He kept looking up at each person who came past, and knew he was probably coming across as creepy, or pervy, or nervous. Or all three. He wasn't sure that he *wasn't* all three.

'Just calm down,' he told himself. 'It's only a date! A nice, ordinary date with a woman. Be nice to her, don't do anything stupid, and get out with your dignity intact. Being nervous isn't going to help either of you.'

He felt his breath tighten. If only it would begin!

He turned and smiled broadly as he saw his date coming out from under some trees on the other side of the clearing. His webbed hand straggled up in a sort of half-wave, then halted as he realized it wasn't her at all, which left him standing there making a sort of fey salute. He felt idiotic, afraid he was directing a ghastly leer at this poor, unsuspecting woman, who hurried away into the night.

He was sure that sweat patches were spreading from the armpits of his shirt.

Thinking the street empty, he tried to force a convincing smile but all he could manage was something like a grimace of despair. Then he heard his name and swivelled.

'Hi!' he squeaked.

'You know, they always say you should order the second-cheapest wine on the menu, that's where they hide their best one,' said the princess, 'because that's the one everyone orders, not wanting to look cheap.'

'Yes, I heard that,' the frog said. 'But actually most restaurants, they don't want to serve something bad, er, as, house wine. Although, we could have . . . What do you like? What would *you* like?'

'You know,' she said. 'You're much taller in real life than I thought you would be from your picture. But I guess that didn't really have anything in it for scale.' She swallowed. 'I'm terribly nervous. I hate first dates. Let's just get a bottle of house white and enjoy it, and try to relax.'

He ordered it, his inner pressure meter subsiding to merely panicked. Whether she really was nervous or not he didn't know, but she had obviously noticed that *he* was and had the sensitivity to draw the attention away from it. A generous impulse. As the waiter withdrew, the frog smiled sincerely for the first time.

'I don't normally come to this part of the forest,' he said.

'I *know*,' she replied. 'Isn't it *funny*? All these quirky little places I never knew about.'

'Some lovely little shops. Nice food joints.'

'LOL, tell me about it,' she said.

'Of course,' he said, knowing he was inserting this somewhat stiffly into the conversation, 'I usually spend almost all of my time on the far side of the lake, towards the swamp. Frogtown.'

She nodded.

'That's where my family's from,' he said. 'I like to see them a lot. I have a lot of siblings. We get along.'

She wasn't noticeably fazed by this, and nor did she particularly engage with it.

'It's such a big frog neighbourhood,' he went on. 'It's hard to escape. I don't *live* there, but it's still a big part of my life.'

'I hear that,' she said. 'I just love frog culture. Myself.'

'You do, you do.' He nodded. Waited for more.

'The music,' she said.

'The music's good,' he replied.

'The humour.' She smiled. She had quite a smile! He hadn't noticed it before.

'We have our moments,' he said. 'We can be funny.'

'*So* funny,' she replied. 'I'm not so hot on the food, though,' she admitted. She popped an olive in her mouth, then plucked the pit from her lips with her impeccable fingertips.

'The food sucks,' said the frog. He laughed. 'Even *we* don't like the food. That's why I suggested coming here tonight. Ah!' He caught the waiter's eye.

As they ordered, the frog couldn't help sighing inside. By god, yes, it was nice to have a date that was going well. Or, at least, not yet going badly. But now that they had cleared the first hurdle, he could see all the other hurdles stretching ahead of him into the distance.

He drank a glass of wine quickly, then topped up both of

their glasses to hide it. The wine sidled into his bloodstream, and some of his more bitter anxieties started to retreat. He noticed that he was enjoying himself. Relaxing, even.

She doesn't mind that I'm a frog, he thought. *Despite the fact that she's a beautiful woman. What's the deal?*

He had another glass of wine and was starting to feel gregarious, but couldn't entirely quieten this voice.

'So you like frogs?' he blurted. 'It was in your bio. I was intrigued.'

'I do.' She lowered her head and looked up at him with big eyes. There were frogs he knew who would have called that a smoulder.

'But you're a princess,' he said. 'That's a big deal. A big responsibility. A wonderful and a trying one, I would think?'

She made a face, as though it were a glamorous day job she didn't like to discuss. 'TBH, I'd rather talk about something else. Like you,' she said. 'Tell me again about your paintings. Watercolours?'

'Acrylics,' he said. But, while he explained acrylics – with a genuine disbelief that she could be paying attention to something so dull – he realized what it was that was bothering him.

'You're rebelling against your parents,' he told her.

'Doesn't everyone?' she asked.

'OK,' he admitted. 'God knows I have. I've even heard of men – human men – who have run away from arranged marriages and gone incognito to find a wife who loves them for who they are. Your parents want you to marry a prince?'

'I've had it with princes,' said the princess. 'I've seen all the eligible bachelors in Christendom. Handsome ones, clever ones, bald ones, young ones. All rich, all available. They've been bringing me illuminated scrolls day in, day out, since I was fourteen. Where do they find the monks to make the pictures so fast, I want to know? Just flip the page right if you're interested, they say. If not, flip left. And if you show the slightest interest, without fail they immediately send a painting of their willy.' She snapped a breadstick.

'None of them were your sort?' said the frog.

'They're all the same. How can you pick a partner that way? Especially when the bloke's paying the portrait painter? All the services in the kingdom these days just want to connect you with one of four sorts of partner: prince, woodcutter, troubadour or wolf. All variations on a theme of bore or predator. No thank you. Give me a frog any day.'

She stared gloomily at the forest outside the window.

The frog watched her for a moment, unable to think of anything to say except, 'Here comes our food.'

As their dishes arrived at the table, she naturally recovered some of her vivacity.

'So, how many frogs have you dated?' said the frog through a mouthful of linguine.

'A couple,' she replied. 'Hey, isn't this just the most divine soufflé? Have a taste.'

She held out her fork as he leaned forward to try it. Ordinarily, he would have felt self-conscious, but there was something so naturally intimate and reassuring about her manner. She beamed when she saw he loved it.

'It *is* divine.' He smiled at her with his eyes, and felt the golden sensation of his smile being absolutely returned. 'Enchanting,' he said.

The frog had convinced himself early on in this conversation that here was a poor little rich girl going on a date with someone who'd shock her parents. He'd been around the pond a few times, thought he knew a frog-fancier when he saw one. (Frog hags, they were sometimes derogatively termed.)

But over the course of, well, two courses, this princess had shown him that she was the real deal. She wasn't acting out, she wasn't behaving in a beautiful way (like so many beautiful young women do) simply to make someone somewhere else miserable. She was being herself. She truly *wanted* to be with him.

'You seem to be quite a sincere person,' he said.

'That's hardly a compliment.' She blinked at him. 'You were expecting me to be otherwise?'

'I dunno if it's not a compliment,' he replied. 'People usually put on one persona or another when they're on a date, don't they?'

'And you aren't?' she asked.

He smiled and looked away. 'You got me. Maybe I am.'

'I hope not,' she said, and she reached forward and took his webbed hand in hers.

He was amazed he'd left it where it could be taken. He stared down at her hand on his.

'I hope you are just like this all the time,' she said. 'That's the sort of man I want to meet.'

'Well,' he said, but he coughed at the same time, and

it became a throaty, strangled cough. He took a drink of water, then asked, 'Shall we get the bill and go for a walk?'

'I'd like that,' she said.

The lake water glimmered under the moon as they walked along, hand in hand.

'This has been really special for me,' the frog said. 'I hate to admit it, but I don't tend to meet people who, ah, *get* me.'

'Me *either*,' she said. 'I couldn't agree more.'

Oh jeeziz, he thought.

After all this time, after all the princesses who just wanted to annoy their parents. Either with him, a drug-addled troubadour who played endless solos on his lute, or some lunkheaded, sawdusty woodcutter. Finally, a real, true-hearted princess. Someone who wants me instead of my damn cousin Peppe.

'Who?' the princess asked.

'Did I say that out loud?'

'Just something about your "damn cousin Peppe".'

'Oh, well. Forget about him. Ha! You'd hate him. Nasty brute. Treats women real bad. He really *is* a frog. Tried it on with the wrong witch and she cursed him. Stuck like that forever.'

'What do you mean "really a frog"?'

'Forget that,' he said. 'Just kiss me.'

He took her other hand and pulled her close. Their lips met, and the surrounding water lilies trembled along with the surface of the lake and the air all around them. A magical charge that had been building dispersed itself in a wonderful frisson.

And the princess found herself standing hand in hand with a boyishly handsome prince.

'Where did my date go?' she asked.

'What? It's me. I'm me! I mean, I'm him!' the prince said.

'But you're *not* him,' she said.

The prince squeezed her hands and smiled. 'But I *am*. I'm him! You transformed me with your kiss! I didn't want to meet someone who loved me just for being a prince, but for who I *truly* am.'

The princess let go. She suddenly looked tired and defeated. She turned away, muttering something. 'I'm calling an Ogre,' she said.

'But we had a good time!' the prince said. 'Didn't we? I know I did. A great time!'

'I asked if you were really a frog,' she said. 'You promised you were.'

The prince had no answer to this. In one evening, he had finally found the thing he most wanted, and then had it taken away again. Unable to laugh or cry, he sat down on the decking and dangled his legs in the lake. She couldn't even look at him as her ogre circled round in his boat to pick her up and take her back to the palace. The prince thought he saw her flick away a tear.

'I'm sorry,' he said to her retreating back.

But she had already pulled the enormous dating catalogue out of her handbag, and was busy flipping the pages left. Looking for a real frog. In a world of dickheads.

THE
PIED PIPER
OF HAMELIN

It was when he did a bit less piping – and after
he did the ice bucket challenge – that his
followers really started to get going.

In the town of Hamelin, a problem had been brewing for years. It came to a head when a small child was bitten by a rat and went green, then puce, and presently died.

'That's terrible,' said the mayor when he was told. 'Appalling news. Wait – which one died? The child or the rat?'

He addressed this question to the visibly distraught mother standing in front of him. Then nodded and said, 'The child. Of course. Accept my condolences, madam. We shall have to give this problem our full attention. Don't worry. Leave it with us.'

He showed the woman out, then turned to his chief advisor who was also, in roughly this order, his clerk, his cook, his cleaner, his mixed boules partner and his wife.

'Sticky,' he said. 'Looks like the time has come. Clearly sudden action is called for.'

A few hours later, many miles away in another small town, a youngish chap was woken from a pleasant snooze in his chair by a tweet notifying him that he'd received a direct message.

He opened his window and plucked the note from the bird's ankle. He read it, replied with a flourish of the quill, then returned to his nap.

A while later, another slightly sturdier pigeon landed on his window ledge with a longer message.

This process continued for some time and was rather messy and repetitious, but the gist of it can be condensed into bullet points:

- The town of Hamelin was desperately in need of one of those Pied Piper fellers you occasionally heard about – who got rid of things.
- Bernard (the youngish chap) was not actually a fully qualified Pied Piper as such, and was really only keeping the office open while his superior was . . . erm, absent. 'Ostrich-sized,' his mother had said. He didn't look like it to Bernard but his mother was insistent. 'He's been totally ostrich-sized,' she said. 'And he's no one to blame but himself.' She seemed to mean he wouldn't be back any time soon. And seeing that his mother was always telling him to have some ambition in life, Bernard accepted the Hamelin assignment.
- This was welcome news, and would he arrive by the next coach?
- He would, so long as they understood that he was not *strictly* a Pied Piper, the office's spare pipe having been recently impounded along with everything else by the police on their fruitless search for the notorious 'cave'. But his cousin did have a recorder he could borrow for a penny. Would that work?

- That was fine, the residents of Hamelin assured him, so long as he would please confirm he would be there as soon as possible. On the next coach, if possible.
- Also, his uniform was not really *pied*, as such. Apart from a gravy stain over the left nipple, it was entirely clean. In fact, some people occasionally mistook it for pyjamas.
- The residents of Hamelin, with scarcely contained frustration, insisted this posed no serious obstacle. So long as he would *please* confirm that he would be on the next . . .

And so on.

Scarcely two days later, in his first appearance as a Pied Piper (or, to be precise, Pyjama'd Recorder-player), Bernard presented himself at the mayor of Hamelin's office. He laid out all available services and applicable rates, and asked what it was that the mayor wanted charmed.

'Charmed?' replied the mayor.

'Yes. Or "got rid of", if you prefer. Mostly I use music and dance, sometimes chanting or whispering. We do all sorts. Snakes, otters, wild horses. I done a plague of locusts once,' he lied. He didn't know what a locust was; he thought it was probably something like an owl.

'Children,' said the mayor. 'There's too many of the little buggers. We're overrun. They keep getting bitten by the rats.'

'Okey-doke,' said Bernard. He was committed to getting his first job on the books.

It seemed to be a very busy day at the mayoral office, with much toing and froing, and many things to be signed, and important people to be spoken to or to be spoken to by. However, when Bernard made his next comment, everyone and everything stopped dead.

'May it please your lordship,' he said, fiddling with his earlobe, 'have you thought about getting rid of the rats?'

'The *rats*?' said the mayor. 'You dare say that in *this* place? Why, our economy would collapse!'

It was clear that all those in the vicinity agreed.

'What would this town be without the rats?' asked a nearby official.

'That's all people come here for,' said the mayor. 'Why do you think the two main pubs here are called The Handsome Scientist and The Surprisingly Tall and Dashing Scholar of Rat Studies? Our species of rat, with its distinctive curly ear, is named after Hamelin, and can only be found here. It's why we are a UFESCO World Site of Ecological Importance! We can't lose *that*. Then we'd be no better than Flingensberg! Their only claim to fame is some princess who pees on hundreds of mattresses or some such distasteful nonsense.'

At the mention of Flingensberg, several clerks and officials instinctively turned and expectorated into the office spittoon.

'Now,' the mayor said to Bernard, 'my, er, brass polisher will show you where to begin your work. And, when she gets back, she can clean out that spittoon. It's getting disgusting.'

*

'It was the lawyers that did it,' said the mayor's wife, as she led Bernard across town. 'First, there was trouble with the local families who kept having children eaten by rats. Then, a load of animal rights campaigners moved in, and got lawyers involved. They sued the town for not protecting the rats' rights.'

'Ah. Quite a mess,' said Bernard.

'Mess is one word,' she said. 'Well, here we are. Most kids play in this slum. Good luck. What's that?'

'My recorder,' said Bernard.

'What are you going to do with that?' she asked.

'My job,' said Bernard stoutly.

'What century are you in?' she asked. 'Kids these days aren't going to listen to no little recorder. You new at this?'

Bernard declined to answer because he was determined not to fail at his first job. Thanking the mayor's wife, he set to work trying to attract the attention of the children.

At first, he danced and sang and played his recorder. This got a few of the less discerning followers. Next, he did the puke-bucket challenge, which got a big laugh and a few more followers. He then did pranks, and made a huge part of his act the performance of 'fails'. He did various other challenges too: tried to swallow a teaspoon of cinnamon; electrocuted himself; ate a selection of the hottest chilli peppers in the world; put on a blindfold and walked around falling over stuff. It was physically demanding, but he could see he was getting somewhere.

He transitioned to regular diary-style content. He wandered around town, saying the first thing that came into his head. The kids lapped it up. Some of them even started to join in.

Still, there were lots of children yet to be won over. He refused to give up.

He found some cats that did very cute tricks, such as playing the recorder for him and getting trapped in bread bins. He did nothing but play a game called Minecraft, which proved inexplicably successful. He learned to specialize in make-up tutorials. He unboxed things – it didn't really matter what. His number of followers doubled, and then doubled again.

It was incredible – this job was possible after all. A piper's life for he!

With his crowd of followers, he danced and pranced his way out of town.

He led them to another town a few miles away, where a sorcerer had cursed all the adults with sterility. The townspeople were overjoyed to see Bernard and his charges. They welcomed the children, promising to protect them and love them, and never to hire pipers or recorder players – whether pie-covered or pyjama-wearing – to take them away again.

Bernard slept in a barn that night. He staggered back into Hamelin a few days later, exhausted but happy, and presented himself at the mayor's office. That mighty personage was once again surrounded by factotums who all wore the selfsame expression of outrage.

'What the bloody hell you thought you were doing is beyond me!' said the mayor.

Bernard gritted his teeth, sensing his fee slipping away from him. 'You asked me to get rid of the children,' he said.

'I'm not interested in raking over old conversations,' the mayor replied. 'All I know is that I've been hit with another lawsuit, this time from the representatives of those children. They're insisting that the children have been unfairly displaced and their rights infringed, of all things! *How* can you have allowed such a thing to happen?'

Bernard explained that he had acted with diligence, handing the children over to responsible adults, and detailed the promises he had elicited from the new parents to love and nurture their new offspring.

'You got them to sign NDAs, of course?' said the mayor. 'Give them to me. We'll deal with this.'

'What's an endy-ai?' asked Bernard. Then he added guardedly, 'Is this going to affect my fee?'

The mayor broke into laughter. A half-beat afterwards, all his workers did too. Then he stopped suddenly and regarded Bernard with a stern expression. So did everyone else.

'An NDA is a "not do anything" form,' the mayor said. His wife whispered in his ear.

'Oh, well. It doesn't matter what the letters stand for! It's legalese for the fact they can't sue us. Mayors use them all the time, I thought they were common knowledge.'

Bernard apologized for this oversight and asked what was to be done.

'Get rid of the rats, dear boy! And toot sweet, chummy! Or your arse will be roasted on the town rotisserie and

encased in pastry. Then you really WILL be a pied piper!
Ha!'

'Is that actually what pied piper means?' Bernard asked.
'It's just I *thought* it was to do with pies, only when I say
that people look at me funny –'

'GET OUT!' bellowed the mayor.

Now, Bernard felt he really had his work cut out for him.
He ventured to the places where the rats congregated, and
started playing his recorder, but there was nothing doing.

He went back to his old material. Not much of it worked.
The cat stuff won him a few dozen followers, but he quickly
ran out of cats.

He thought hard.

Once again, he started playing pranks on people. They
worked after a fashion – the meaner, the better. He started
attacking townspeople, doing take-down reviews of them,
calling them out on their perceived failings.

Things started to pick up.

Companies for whom rats were a big market – cheese
manufacturers, refuse-dump builders and so on – started
paying to advertise in Bernard's performances.

Then he changed tack. He began making angry
speeches with edgy allusions to 'the new world order' and
the secret powers that ran it. The trick was to hint heavily
about what was going on, then claim to leave his audience
to make up their own minds.

He blamed everything on witches (he said all women
were witches), and his following surged. So he really
leaned in to this sort of rhetoric, inveighing against the

sort of multi-speciesism that had led to towns being so crowded in the first place.

The rats loved this. God, they loved it.

He blamed people. He blamed governors. He implied that he and the rats were all being screwed over and destroyed by the elites in their above-ground houses (what lent his performance some conviction was his now relative certainty he wouldn't be paid).

He was practically living in the sewer now.

And, finally, all of the rats were following him.

He led them out into the countryside, planning to release them there.

But he realized the rats loved him too much. He had given them something to live for. And they wouldn't leave him.

He intuitively knew the next step was to make promises to his followers, to tell them that violence was inevitable. If he didn't step up the rhetoric, they would have time to start thinking, and perhaps doubt him. And what would they do to him then? He was sure he'd seen skeletons down there in the sewers, stripped of flesh. No doubt they belonged to humans who had displeased the rats – he tried not to think about it.

So he converted his fear into energy. He declared the beginning of what he called the Vermin Wars. We've reclaimed the word vermin, he told them. From now on, the word 'human' will mean what that word used to mean.

By now, of course, he had long been eating their food and living among them.

You can get used to anything, it turns out. Because one

day he woke up and realized that he no longer wanted the rats to go. He had nothing without them.

After all the vicious things he'd said about humans, he could not return to human society anyway. He saw now that he was, *thoroughly*, ostrich-sized.

But why return to being an impoverished Pyjama'd Recorder-player anyway, when you could be king of the rats? He would do anything to stop them leaving.

He was starting to love them.

They were him, and he was them.

There you go. Just a story. With no parallels in our world at all. Ho-hum!

RED
RIDING
HOOD

'Teeth, tits and tail.'

When Red Riding Hood got her first order of the day, she was lying on the lice-infested straw mattress in her tiny room in SoFo (short for South Forest), by far the cheapest district in all of Fairyland. A place where desperate young folk started out, and knackered old creatures ended up.

But Red knew that if she was to get away from the area, she had to earn it. So, the second she got an order notification, she jumped up and headed outside, checking the details on her way.

Order #264614
Pick-up location: Three Bears Cottage B & B
Items: 3 x 24-box assorted doughnuts
Deliver to: Pigtons Estate Agents

There was a rank of rental ponies, lined up in their branded orange livery, just down the road from her apartment. She fed a bronze coin into the machine, and the ankle-lock on one of the beasts popped open.

'Hello, darling!' Red said. She loved meeting new ponies. It was one of the best parts of her day. She rubbed the pony behind the ears and kissed it a few times on the cheek, then she flicked up her hood, hopped on the pony's back, and set off at speed. Must be quick. There was always so little time.

There were things Red loved about being an Ogre Eats delivery rider. Lots of fresh air and exercise. Meeting new people (and ponies). The occasional freebie when picking up near to closing time. And, best of all, providing a community service by delivering food to folks who weren't mobile.

But there were some serious downsides too. You must never stray from the path, even by accident, or you weren't covered by Ogre Eats's insurance. Also, you had to make a certain number of deliveries per day or else you started to lose money on your rental pony, and there were days when the orders just didn't come in. Some lucky delivery persons might have been bought a pony by Mummy and Daddy, but most had to sweat their guts out just to eat. (Red was living on foraged salad leaves and roadkill while she tried desperately to save up for her own pony.)

Then there was *that* ad campaign. The Ogre Eats tagline – 'Fancy something delicious tonight? That's the way the ogre eats!' – was famous and well loved, but a recent commercial had put them into the kind of soup they *didn't* boast about delivering in thirty minutes or less. The ad opened on a monstrous ogre towering over a sacrificial virgin, who was screaming for mercy. Then, right at the moment when the ogre seemed about to satisfy his hunger, they both turned to face the audience, grinning and giving a thumbs-up in echo of the Ogre Eats logo.

When it aired, the backlash was swift and brutal. The

ad perpetuated problematic ogre stereotypes, on top of which no ogres had been sought for the role. The company looked bad, thoughtless and behind the times. They withdrew the ad, fired their head of marketing, apologized and donated a large sum to a home for elderly ogres, but really it was too late. Everyone was already upset and angry with each other, and there was no taking the insult back.

It seemed another one of these fights came along every week. Whether it was the shoemaker being accused of trafficking elfs, or the elfs being pilloried in the right-wing press for unionizing; whether it was gingerbread men being awarded the right to buy the gingerbread houses they had built for sundry witches (now burned); or whether it was the serving of sashimi at the Little Mermaid's wedding that turned out to be distant relatives of hers; nowadays the whole of Fairyland seemed to be rocked by perpetual scandal and outrage. Some suspected Prussian interference in the matter.

In this case the brouhaha, if I may use the word, and I don't see why not, it's my book after all, died down after a week. But, months later, delivery riders like Red were still being buttonholed by members of the public on one side of the argument or other, and lectured about it. It certainly wasn't Red's fault, and only added to her stress. She just wanted to be kind and respectful to everyone.

'Ogre Eats!' she yelled, pushing through the crush inside Three Bears. 'Picking up!'

No one heard her.

Jeez, Red thought. *This place is doing pretty well for itself.* Every time she picked up from here, it seemed to have doubled its clientele.

''Scuse me! Watch out!' She elbowed her way up to the counter. 'Ogre Eats delivery rider!'

Daddy Bear handed her a paper package. It seemed just a few weeks ago this place only did porridge. Now there was a full menu on the wall.

Red smiled at Daddy Bear but he was too busy to notice. In the kitchen beyond, Red could see Mummy Bear conducting an orchestra of pans and kettles, while their son skated around taking orders.

Good to see bears making out in this economy, Red thought as she forged her way back through the crowds to the door.

Seeing a clear stretch of path ahead of her, Red accelerated to a gallop and turned towards the business district, where Pigtons was located.

'Slow down, you maniac!' yelled the seven dwarfs, leaping aside as she rounded the corner.

'Sorry!' she yelled. 'Love the podcast!'

'Don't mind us!' called Gretel and Hansel, waving and smiling as she swerved round them.

Those two look much healthier, Red thought. *Used to deliver to their house a lot. Now, not so much . . .*

Descending into a combe, she angled left towards the business district at breakneck pace. Now she was really enjoying herself.

When Red reached the offices of Pigtons, the receptionist

(smiling so hard you'd think her face would break) asked if she'd mind delivering straight to the meeting room. Red sauntered in and put the package down, taking out three trays of doughnuts and placing them along the table. (It seemed rude to just dump the order and leave.) The pigs barely noticed her, though; they were transfixed by the screen at the end of the room.

'By the end of the next calendar year,' the eldest pig, the one in spectacles, was saying, 'we expect to reach saturation point in all areas of the forest. The *following* year, with three more offices opening in the capital city, our *real* expansion across the whole of Fairyland begins.'

All of the pigs nodded hungrily, and Red silently withdrew.

Look at them all in the office on a Saturday, she thought as she headed back outside. *There really is no stopping the spread of Pigtons.*

As she got to the pony, another order came in. This time, the pick-up was from Blando's (Red shuddered) and was going to nearby Silicon Hillock.

Half an hour later, Red was parking up by a delivery bay at the back of a large office building. It looked thoroughly empty for the weekend, but her hesitant knock was answered at once by a young woman whose stunning good looks were spoiled by neither the grubbiness of her overalls nor the dust on her face.

'Cinderella?' Red asked.

The woman gave a winning smile, took the food and gave a big tip.

Behind her, dragging a sack of recycling over each shoulder across the delivery bay, was a young man Red could have sworn was a very sweaty and vexed-looking Prince Charming. But obviously it couldn't be.

Red stopped at a nearby gas station (so-named because couriers stood around gossiping while their rides refilled) for a welcome breather, but it wasn't long before another order came in.

Red sighed. The destination was up in the hills, miles from anywhere. At least the pick-up was nearby – a quaint little delicatessen by the lake near Frogtown. The package clinked with the recognizable sound of wine bottles as Red put it in her pannier and she caught the eye of a glamorous woman standing nearby. They smiled at each other.

'I'm delivering it, I promise,' said Red.

'Could do with a glass myself,' said the woman. 'Waiting for my date to arrive.'

'Have a good one,' said Red.

The woman sighed anxiously and gave a brave smile. 'Hopefully this time,' she said.

In a few minutes Red was up in the hills. The pony cantered happily, and Red felt the wind in her hair as the countryside rushed past. It felt like flying.

But as she climbed higher, the gloom of the woods crept in around her. It was nearly sunset and the canopy was thick. The houses – all ex-council cottages in this area – became fewer and farther between. You heard rumours of things happening to people up here.

Red locked her pony to a tree just off the way and looked around. The woods were eerily silent. Her destination was a hundred yards or so back from the road, at the end of a long path. She approached the front door of the cottage, package in hand, shrugging off the sense she was being watched. She took a breath, then knocked.

'Ogre Eats!' she called. 'Delivery!'

'Please come in, dearie,' a frail voice called from inside. 'I'm not particularly mobile.'

Red tentatively pushed at the door. It swung inwards.

'"Grandma"?' Red asked. That was the name she'd been given.

'Over here,' came the voice.

'Is there a candle or something? I can't make out –'

A match flared and hovered over a candle, its gentle glow expanding to reveal a bedside table. Then, next to it, a bed. In which lay something that looked to Red like a wolf dressed as a human woman.

'Bring it over here,' said the grandma-wolf.

But Red was rooted to the spot.

'If you will,' the wolf said, smiling. The candle light reflected off its eyes.

Her eyes, Red corrected herself. You didn't call a wolf *it*. What was wrong with her today?

She took one step forward as slowly as she could. Her mind was racing and she struggled to keep up with her thoughts.

First and foremost, here she was, a young woman alone late at night in the house of a wolf. And the wolf was beckoning her forward with a grin. Her mother would have fainted at the very thought.

But then, her mother had been born *a long time ago*. Things had changed. A lot. And then had changed a whole lot more. Red was a right-on liberal to her core and proud of it. You could almost say that she *lived* to be sensitive and kind towards her fellow beings – that, for her, living in a society that welcomed difference instead of abhorring it made life worthwhile.

But that didn't mean she knew what to do and say in every situation.

She took another step closer to the wolf. She tried to smile.

Red thought of those moments when, riding through the forest at top speed, she had caught glimpses of young wolves in the shadows, loitering pounceishly. She felt her smile wobble.

She immediately castigated herself for this thought. She imagined all this wolf had been through: all the casual discrimination, the *deliberate*, brutal bigotry. The exclusionary policies, denial of rights, institutional intolerance, lack of opportunity. The terrible economic hardship.

And still, there she was, sitting in bed and smiling. Red *had* to honour her beliefs and not be scared. She took a moment to recall the facts: this wolf was, roughly, 95 per cent certain not to eat her. The odds were in her favour. To run out of the cottage screaming for her life would only further entrench the sort of suspicion and social division that made the forest a worse place to live.

Then the bottles within the bag clinked and she jumped.

She forced herself to take the last few paces towards the wolf.

And, as she drew closer, she saw her.

The fur was thin, and nearly white. A pair of ever-so-dainty bifocals perched just above the line of her whiskers. Her nightcap was slightly askew, and face down on her lap was a well-thumbed copy of *Wolf and Peace*.

She was what she had first seemed: a grandma, gently spoken and frail. With kind eyes. *How stupid I was*, Red thought, *not to realize that a wolf and someone called Grandma could be the same person.*

Red now noticed the pictures dotted around the walls of the cottage. Family portraits of the wolf with her grandchildren (the likeness was unmistakeable). Photos of the wolf and her pensioner friends at the beach, at bingo, on a cruise ship. Laughing and smiling. Having a great time.

'You wouldn't open it, would you, dearie?' asked the wolf.

'Hmm?' said Red, suddenly realizing that she was there in a professional capacity. 'Oh, yes, of course. I'd be delighted.' She tore open the package to reveal two bottles of red and a delicious-looking cake wrapped in foil.

'And if you would do an old woman a very kind service – would you share it with me?' the wolf asked. 'I'm *quite* alone, after all, and cake's no good eaten alone.'

Red just nodded, too overcome with shame to speak.

She was appalled by the fears she'd entertained until a moment ago. She was so horrified with herself she felt she might cry. She only hoped she'd kept her thoughts adequately hidden.

As Red fetched plates, a knife and some wine glasses from the kitchen, she thought how lucky she was to have met such a person. She must have so many stories to tell, and such resilience. But of course she should really treat the wolf – Grandma – like anyone else. It was disrespectful to do otherwise.

She returned to the bedside, determined to be normal. (*There I go again*, she thought, *what it this hateful word* normal? *'Calm', is what I meant.*) She cut each of them a slice of cake and poured two glasses of wine. She handed one to the wolf.

'I hope you don't mind drinking and riding,' said the wolf.

'Oh, I won't get stopped at this time of night!' Red said gaily. 'And anyway, the paths are empty.' She trusted it was OK to speak this way in front of someone of Grandma's generation. Any of her own friends would have been *deeply* shocked. She certainly had no intention of riding home after drinking (primarily because of the danger to others, obviously, but – good lord, imagine if she lost her riding licence) and would instead call an Ogre, and fetch the pony tomorrow.

They both took a sip of wine.

Grandma let out a deep breath, looking happy and replete.

Red Riding Hood, however, could think of nothing to say. She was trying too hard to appear relaxed and at ease. She desperately wanted to ask Grandma about her struggles but didn't know how to begin.

The wolf saw she was nervous. *Obviously*, she thought, *I appear like some sort of museum piece. Fascinating perhaps, but more or less mummified. Oh well. If awkward silence is all we can have then awkward silence is all there shall be. The wine's good at least.*

'May I say –' Red cleared her throat.

'Yes, dear?'

'What wonderful, large eyes you have.'

Those eyes softened. The wolf relaxed against her pillow. 'You *are* kind to say such a thing.'

'Not at all,' mumbled Red.

They lapsed back into silence.

Look at the poor girl, the wolf thought sadly. *So awkward. But she has no idea how happy she's making me. All these long, lonely nights up here in the woods, with the wind howling . . . She thinks we ought to discuss important issues. I'd rather talk about* Grey's Anatomy. *Maybe I should break the tension.*

'And what large ears I have!' said the wolf.

Red giggled, and Grandma joined in.

'A downside of ageing,' said the wolf, holding her glass out for a refill. 'Ears keep growing. And you can't hide 'em. What d'you call yourself, little one?'

'Red Riding Hood,' she said. 'Red for short.'

'I like it,' said the wolf, tilting her head back to examine Red through the lower half of her specs. 'And why call yourself that?' Now she leaned forward and looked over the top of her glasses. 'What's your given name?'

'Britney,' said Red. They both laughed. Red put her hands over her eyes and shook her head. 'My parents were young,' she said. 'But still, it's hard to forgive.'

Emboldened by the wine, Red looked again at the wolf and said, smiling, 'What large *teeth* you have!'

The temperature abruptly dropped. The wolf's expression went stale.

You can be having such a nice time with one of them, she thought rancorously, *but it's only a matter of time before something unpleasant rears its head.* Referring to the largeness of one's teeth was, of course, vulgar if accidental, and unforgiveable if done on purpose. Forty years ago it was the cliché that people (particularly the nastier brand of comedian) had used to highlight 'difference'.

Red despaired. She knew at once she had said something terribly wrong, even though she'd had no idea such a remark was offensive. But there was no way to explain this without worsening the insult. A moment before she'd been having a friendly drink, and now she was sitting in a stranger's house and acting abominably. All she wanted was to tell the wolf how much she admired her.

The wolf watched as the insensitive little girl swallowed a few sobs, then gathered up the paper package and wine cork, and took her plate into the kitchen in preparation for leaving. Hearing the plate being washed up, her indignation started to lose its fierceness. She saw that this was a person trying hard to be good and kind, let down by ignorance. She *had* stayed to keep an old wolf company, and didn't seem the sort to get a sly dig in.

'Please,' Grandma said as Red came back in, 'don't leave like this. There's still plenty of wine. Let's just have a nice chat.'

And so, a nice chat they had.

Over the next few hours, the wolf and Red talked, sipped wine, and learned more about one another. Warmth returned to the cottage. Although they'd been thrown together by chance, they both began to feel that they were beginning to understand each other.

Red knew that she could only see things from her perspective, and that somewhere in the woods there was a wolf storyteller giving another version of this tale, in which she came across very differently. That was the way it had to be.

The conversation had been special. It felt like one that would have been impossible just a few years ago. And possibly, hopefully, it was a small step forward for the inhabitants of the forest.

When the hour grew late and the wine ran low, Red got up to leave. Dawn was hinting at the edges of the curtains.

As she opened her mouth to say farewell, the door of the cottage burst open.

A tall blond man stood before them. It was the woodcutter.

'I've got reports of a young human missing!' he shouted. (He was also the volunteer police officer in this part of the forest.) 'JESUS! It's the big bad wolf! Get down! Get down!'

Red and the wolf turned towards him with an expression of disgust.

'SOD OFF!' they both yelled.

But the woodcutter showed no sign of hearing. He advanced upon the wolf, his axe raised.

Red saw, with perfect clarity, that any police tribunal would clear the woodcutter of whatever he was about to do. She had to stop him. So, once he got a pace past her, she clocked him over the back of the head with an empty wine bottle. He went down like a sack of spuds.

The wolf got out of bed to help Red haul the unconscious woodcutter outside, and they slung him across the back of his horse, then slapped its behind. It disappeared into the forest, which in the light of the dawn didn't feel anything like so threatening as the night before. It was beautiful, and quiet, and wonderful.

The two women turned to one another and nodded. They shook hands. Then they laughed at their own formality and hugged.

This was *definitely* the beginning of something good.

Which is the best ending that a story can have.

Unless it isn't.

Make up your own mind.

☺

Thanks

Jamie Coleman came up with the idea for this book, and edited it too. I'm extremely grateful, is one understatement that I could make at this point. Also to the other readers at Puffin who gave very helpful advice over multiple readings – Katie Sinfield in particular. Steph Barrett was great too. Good eggs both. In my opinion.

This book's dedicated to my brother, Henry, and his wonderful wife, Juliette. I love you both very much. Henry also happens to be brilliant at coming up with stories like the ones in this book, and giving helpful editorial feedback. His students are very lucky.

I have also run these tales repeatedly past anyone who will listen. Catharine and Roger Vincent are excellent sounding boards. And also parents. Not necessarily in that order. Jordan Whitfield was a really sound guy. Jim Clarke's no idiot. And Ben, Berrak & Brig, Harry Man, Sally Dolton and Ken Perepelkin, Lucy Pessell, Diana Pilkington, Ben Metcalf, Patrick Ferguson, Tom Wharton, Sneha Wharton and Steve Dumughn: I thank you all from the very heart of my bottom.

About the Author

Bruno Vincent is just a bloke. If you've heard of anything he's done before it's probably *Five on Brexit Island*, which isn't published by Penguin so I probably shouldn't go on about it here. Apparently David Cameron has a copy. I hope it chokes him.

From Russia with Likes
The Labradoodle of the Baskervilles
Charlotte's Dark Web
For Whom the Notification Alerts
Tinker, Tailor, Soldier, Graphic Designer
The Selfie of Dorian Gray
Affordable House on the Prairie
Alice Through the Instagram Filter
The Hermes Delivery Man Doesn't Even Ring Once
Anne of Clean Tables: The Autobiography
of a Tidying Guru
Finnegan's Woke
Lady Chatterley's Cleaner: An Unheard Voice
The 39 Steps . . . to a New Beautiful You
A Confederacy of Onesies